Se-lah

When Mommy Left for Farin

DENISE NICHOLSON

"Farin" is a Caribbean dialectal term for the word "foreign".

1

Se-lah (When Mommy Left for Farin)

Published by: Denise Nicholson, In Partnership with Nia Sadé Akinyemi, *The Literary Revolutionary*.

www.knittedtogether2.com.
www.theliteraryrevolutionary.com

ISBN #: 978-0-9968910-9-7

Copyright © 2018 Denise Nicholson

Publisher's Note

Manufactured in the United States of America

Stock Image: CreateHERStock
www.createherstock.com
Editing & Cover Design By: *The Literary Revolutionary*
www.theliteraryrevolutionary.com

Follow Author Denise Nicholson
Facebook.com/AuthorDNicholson
Instagram/Twitter: @KnittedTogether
www.knittedtogether2.com

Se-lah

When Mommy Left for Farin

DENISE NICHOLSON

PUBLISHED IN PARTNERSHIP WITH

The Literary Revolutionary

ATLANTA MIAMI NEW YORK DMV DALLAS

Why Se-Lah?

This book has been in my head for quite a long time. I prayed on the title for the longest, and one morning as I was driving to work "Se-lah" came to me. I can admit, I didn't like the title of the book at first. However, while I was at work that day I met a patient who stated she had never met a nurse like me. She announced that she was a writer and I felt moved to mention to her that I wanted to write a book. I gave her a brief overview of the stories that were in my head; stories that had been with me for a couple of years. That woman instructed me to go home and start the book that day. She encouraged me not to wait ten years from now, but to start right now.

In the car on my way home after work that day, I sat in silence for the 45 minute drive. The name "Se-lah" came to me again, so I looked up the word and it said, "Be still, stop, and listen". Though the message was clear, I didn't find the name "Se-lah" interesting enough. At the time, I had created a list and I used it to add different potential titles. I put Se-lah to the side and kept looking for a name, because I wasn't exactly pleased with it. I was looking to have a catchy name like all the books I'd read before. After searching a short while longer, I got a word from God that said "be obedient. The name is Se-lah."

…and here we are.

Denise Nicholson

Dedication

To my great-grandmother "Didi" Ketura Grant, with love and gratitude, because she taught me the importance of being still, of listening to my inner voice, and the joy of engaging in a good story. She fostered a love of stories in me and that changed my life forever. She made me feel significant and gave me a good reference of being totally and completely loved, which sustained me. This was an important well to draw from when I had children of my own. On the days when I was overwhelmed with life and I didn't want to be patient with my children, I would remember my great-grandmother's gentle tone and reassuring words. Though only a few words, they were enough for me because they reminded me that my responsibility was to overflow my children with love and to teach them to love themselves and their neighbors. I would have been lost without her love.

To my grandmother Irene Dolphy; an entrepreneur and visionary who taught me to be self-reliant and the importance of serving those who are less fortunate than myself. Her wisdom taught me that time really is the master. With time everything changes, and with age everything gets better.

To my mother Merle Dolphy, who had the audacity of hope and dared to leave the comforted pain of her homeland to foster opportunities for herself and her children. Mom, you were among many who in droves left your children behind for a world of disillusion. I am a product of your pursuit of happiness. Your losing your life set me on a path that eventually led me to triumph in mine.

To all the women who helped to raise me including my paternal grandmother, whom I lovingly call Nana – I can only imagine how life would have been for me if you were not among the pioneers and warriors who came before and paved a way for me and for my children. I love you and will do my duty to impart the lessons you've shared. My gratitude to you will be made evident in my continued service to the underprivileged of future generations.

To the board members of the group Knitted Together, we found a good thing; a place for us to learn, grow, and a space where others can tell their stories and begin to heal. We found a community that gives voice to all who have a need to be heard.

Table of Contents

Acknowledgements

I am grateful to all who came together to help me write this book. My husband Adrian, for his support and encouragement and his delicious meals; my children Adrian, Phillip, and Ariel, for recognizing when I needed assistance and jumping right in and helping me to balance the rest of my life; my grandchildren Noah and Noelle, for their patience and love; my partner publisher Nia Sadé Akinyemi, for her incredible patience, dedication, and hard work. I want to offer a special thanks to Dr. Avon Connell whose commitment to excellence, helped me produce a book that I am proud of.

I am indebted to my third-grade teacher, Ms. Attaberry, who saw something in me and made me feel like everything I did was a big deal. Your kind words and encouragement influenced almost everything I accomplished. I am also indebted to the women whose stories influenced this fictional book.

Life is a journey. Along the way, listen without judgment to what others have to say, show kindness and love every chance you get and the world will be a better place.

Road Trip

As I laid in the grogginess of my sleep, I heard the wailing sound of the alarm clock. With my eyes still shut and my body feeling heavy with the weight of yesterday's work, I reached towards the sound with one hand, barely moving from under the warmth of the fluffy comforter. I felt my way across the top of the Bose radio to press the snooze button. Instantly, I realized it was the day I had been anticipating for quite some time.

I couldn't believe this day was finally here; the day for my long deserving girl's trip. I planned to work only half the day. Since the doctor is usually busy on Friday mornings and I am the only nurse practitioner who works with him on Fridays, he asked another practitioner to come in for the other half of the day to

13

help out. We agreed that we would schedule patients starting at 7 a.m. to get a two-hour head start so that I could leave at 1 p.m.

After I mentally reviewed the day in my head, I said my prayers, and did my final stretches. I rolled my entire body on top of my husband's since he was already awake and had started his morning routine; checking the Huffington Post on his IPhone. I kissed him good morning and hopped out of bed. As soon as my feet touched the cold, hardwood floor, I got chills. Excitedly, I threw my covers to the side and practically skipped towards the bathroom. Meeting my reflection in the mirror I said to myself, "Today is going to be a great day."

The morning turned out to be more eventful than I planned, as one of my patients had an extremely high blood pressure and had to be rushed by ambulance to the emergency department. Compounding the issue was her refusal to go with the EMT. She was kicking and screaming on the stretcher. Meanwhile, the EMTs tried their best to calm her down so she wouldn't stroke out.

"I can't go to the ER again!" She yelled.

"That's why I came here! To see you, my primary. Damn! If I wanted to go to the ER, I wudda went straight from the Rheumatologist office, when he told me my blood pressure was high!" She was wailing on us. "I have things to do! Who gon' pick up my grandbaby from school? Somebody gotta call my daughter!" she complained.

"Ms. Mona, you must go to the emergency department because the medicine I have given you is not working fast enough and I don't want you to have a stroke." I explained in a low, but firm tone. "Now please, let go of the railing so these gentlemen can take you to the hospital and get you the help you need." She followed my instructions taking her hand off of the rail, but continued pointing and shouting.

"Call my daughter! Call my daughter! Call my daughter!" She screamed. Before the men rolled her out of the office on the stretcher, one of the secretaries told us she had gotten in touch with the patient's daughter. "Ms. Mona," she started, "I've already called Shavonne. She will pick up your grandbaby from school and meet you at the hospital."

The sound of wheels on the clinic floor faded away soon after the good news. Now that Ms. Mona was all set, I had to get my notes done so I could get out of the office and pick up the nine seater truck that I rented for the trip before 5 p.m. Considering that I got a head start on the day, I wasn't even worried about the time. I took a quick glance at the clock and saw that it was just a quarter to nine. *Yes!* I thought to myself. Just a few more hours and I'm out of here.

I settled back in my office and started tapping away on my computer. I was on with my notes. The next time I glanced at the clock, I gave it the evil eye. Just one more note to type and I was out! As my luck would have it, even with extra help I ended up working the whole shift. I don't know where the patients were coming from, but it seemed we were beginning to get new ones every hour.

My son kept texting me to see if I was finally ready to leave work and when I was, he was right on time to pick me up. Thank goodness!

"What happened to your, *'I'm leaving at the stroke of 1 o'clock!'*?"

"Oh my goodness! You wouldn't believe the drama today."

"Murphy's law. It's always something when you have someplace to go or a deadline to meet. We'll make it though. I already called the rental company and told them we were on our way."

I looked at my son and smiled. "You're the best. I love you."

We drove over to the rental car place. The truck I'd reserved was a beautiful black Cadillac Escalade. It was huge! I climbed into the truck to check it out and get familiar with the thing. It had gorgeous black leather seats that were smooth to the touch with cup holders everywhere. The trunk space was impressive and it looked like it could hold all of our luggage. Feeling the interior as I moved throughout the vehicle, I was suddenly hit with a wretched smell. The car reeked of vomit!

I was livid.

After I expressed to the rental car staff that I was not driving ten hours with the smell of vomit in the air, the manager decided to have someone clean it. Frustration arose within me as I was already late. Now

I had to wait on them to clean the car. I told my girlfriends I would pick them up and we could head out before it got dark, yet here it was already 6 p.m. I quickly updated our WhatsApp group chat and told the girls what was going on. I let them know that I would be on my way soon. *Lies.*

By the time they finished scrubbing all the mats in the car, I was another thirty minutes behind. My son spoke to the manager and convinced him to give me a discount for the inconvenience. After the car cleaning and an extra thirty percent discount, I drove the truck behind my son's car and we headed home.

Back at the house I grabbed my bag that I had packed the night before. I walked over to my husband and ran the palms of my hands on his five o'clock shadow, gave him a tight hug, and kissed him goodbye. He slapped me on my butt and tenderly whispered, "Look out for the idiots on the road, do not text and drive, and stop at a rest stop when you get tired to take a twenty minute nap." He then loaded my one carry-on size suitcase into the back of the truck, and waited until I pulled out of the driveway before turning toward the house. I was only a few seconds out of my neighborhood on my way to get the girls when my phone rang.

"Where you at?" True spoke over the phone.

"I'm on my way." I answered with one hand on the steering wheel and the other holding my phone as I put it on speaker.

"Girl, we've been waiting from the time you said you were on your way the first time." She complained.

"I'm in traffic. It's Friday." I retorted.

When I got to True's house, which was the designated meeting place because of its central location, the only person there was True.

"I thought you said you all were ready," I stressed, looking around.

"Check the group chat." She said, strutting towards the car with all the attitude in the world. "I can't with y'all."

True piled her two big bags in the car, knowing we had a one bag per person policy. I just shook my head. I barely could get the keys in the ignition before True turned the radio off, forcing me to listen to her complaints.

"Tasha asked for us to pick her up at her house, and the Connecticut girls said they're stuck in traffic. The friends you invited said they were on their way an hour ago." She jerked her head around and looked at me. "Where the hell they coming from?" The perfect wind interrupted and blew her hair as an added effect it seemed, to the melodramatic performance she was putting on.

"I've been packed and ready to go since 3 o'clock." She emphasized by putting up three fingers. She continued to rant. We bickered some more and then headed to get Tasha.

"This is nice," True said, snapping back into character. She had just realized we were in a brand new Escalade and the details of the car distracted her. Thank God!

We pulled up to Tasha's house and I went inside to find her crawling on all fours, bumping into her furniture like a blind dog looking for a bone. "What are you doing crawling around on the floor?"

"I'm looking for my boot." She answered.

"Okay, you have two minutes to meet me in the car. If you're not there, I'm out."

She couldn't find one of her shoes that she swears is so comfortable she would die if she didn't bring them. We were running late, so I did what any good friend would do in this situation. I got in the car and gave her two minutes to get her shit in the trunk. While waiting I pulled out my phone and updated WhatsApp with Tasha's shenanigans. The Connecticut girls had finally arrived at the meeting spot. After having already travelled almost two hours in traffic, they had no patience for Tasha and her missing shoe and True had an attitude because we were running late.

I started to drive off after waiting two minutes when I saw Tasha run out her house and toward the car with one boot on her foot. The other, with a curled up toe, she raised in the air like a trophy and her bag was hauled on one shoulder like a hamper. "I got it, I got it!" She yelled. True nearly fell out the car laughing.

"Where the hell you going with those ugly ass donkey looking boots? I thought you were in there looking for some damn red bottoms or summ," True screeched while trying to catch herself from falling out the car as she threw her head back with laughter.

"Leave me alone. Dem very comfatable. Open di trunk mek mi put mi tings in. Let's go!"

I was too through with Tasha for having us wait on her to find those ugly ass boots that looked like "kick me, kill me."

We drove back to True's house, the original meeting point, where everyone should have been waiting. I picked up the Connecticut girls who are my sisters, Rachelle and Rain. My friends Joy and Amy from the Bronx were now with them. Now, we could get on the road to North Carolina.

Once inside, all the ladies talked about how big and luxurious the truck was and how we needed to rent luxury cars more often. Surprisingly, the traffic was smooth and light all the way to Virginia. It started to rain in Delaware and I could barely see through the fog on the windshield, but True drove an Escalade years ago and she claimed to know a thing or two about the truck's function. True fidgeted with the settings and turned on the defogger and the problem went away. We made one stop in Maryland when Rachelle insisted she had to pee. Even though it was night, Rain demanded that we take pictures and a video with her new GoPro camera at the rest stop.

"This camera is bad! You should see the underwater footage the kids got when they went to visit their grandmother in Florida." Rain exclaimed.

"Well I hope you know I'm not going in no water." True said as she patted her hair, pouted her lips, and posed for the camera. "I had my hair in flexi rods for two days, just so these curls could last the whole weekend." She said flipping one of her curls.

"You wearing a damn wig!" Rain declared. "Just take it off if they have a pool; you ain't fooling none of us." We all laughed because the way True was flipping her hair, anyone would have thought that it was all her natural hair.

I got gas and coffee and we all took a bathroom break before heading back on the road. Everyone brought something back; gum, mixed nuts, chips, you name it. I guess because I was the driver they felt they needed to bribe me to stay alive. "I'm doing 80 miles anyway," I told them. "Y'all better stay your asses up."

True decided she would sit in the front because she was the co-pilot and she swore that she would stay awake. "I'll be up with you. I'm just glad I ain't the one driving this long ass trip. Shit, my back hurting me already just thinking about it. I got you though."

By the time we got to Maryland her ass was snoring. I was glad to have my snacks, and Amy to talk to while all the other girls were asleep. I met Amy when I was a nurse at a family clinic, before I became a nurse practitioner. She was both a secretary and medical assistant. We got close during the days as she focused mainly on taking the patient's information, and calling insurance companies when needed to get approvals for visits. She stocked the office, placed orders, verified receipts, and did all things related to the role of a medical assistant. In the evenings when all the patients and secretary had gone for the day, she would file papers and set up the office for the next day. Since the patient traffic moved through so quickly, I always needed to stay to write my notes, which is when Amy and I found time to talk and share our lives.

Amy talked about her parents all the time; this time was no different. While everyone was sleeping, she shared plans to build them a house in her home country of Trinidad. She told me she recently and secretly married one of the doctors who worked in the hospital above the clinic. Her mother and father were coming to visit so they could meet him. She was so excited that her mother was coming from Trinidad to see her, that she dismissed the fact that she had just told me she got married. *I know she's not acting like she didn't just tell me she got married, and to a fucking doctor.*

"Wait, wait, wait the fuck up! You just got what?"

"Married." She answered.

"Do I know him?!" I screamed.

"I don't know." She said shyly.

"What tha hell!? You couldn't tell me you were getting married?"

"Noooo, we just wanted to keep it a secret because his ex-wife works in the emergency department and he didn't want a scandal."

"What, he has an ex-wife? Do I know her?"

"I don't knooow!" she whined in her baby voice.

"She's a nurse in the ED." Amy said.

"That means I have given her a report before. What's her name?"

"You can't say anything if I tell you." Amy said, looking at me intently.

"So tell me his name, because I don't know if I can promise you that." My eyes were on the road, but my mind was ready for her to spill the beans already!

"You know the tall, Jewish doctor from gastro, and his father is the head of the department?"

"Dr. Rothenstein?! Of course I know him! Everybody knows him. He likes black girls? But he wears a yarmulke!"

"Yup dat one!"

"You are kidding me right now! Does he take it off during sex?"

"Sometimes; depending on where we doing it."

"You are sooooo nasty Amy."

23

"Yup." She was so nonchalant with it. Who knew Amy had this side to her? Obviously she wasn't ashamed.

"He was married to another black woman?" I asked, not finished with her just yet.

"Nope, she's Jewish."

"What?! Oh my Goodness girl! You stole that white lady's husband!" I put both hands on the steering wheel and sat all the way up. I was definitely wide awake now.

"Not me. I just met him and he had been divorced two years before I met him." She was always so calm.

"Didn't I always tell you though this was going to happen to you? Cause you are fine as hell and you are so friggin smart!" I said reassuringly. Amy was always a bit timid and humble, so I just asked another question to take some of the pressure off of her. "He was married to someone in the emergency department?"

"Yup, but it didn't work out." She said this with no sense of shade in her tone. Shoot, better than me.

"They have children?"

"Yup, two." She said, while raising her two fingers as she looked at me through the rearview mirror.

"What? That is a scaaaandal girl!! I'm so happy for you though. I could pull over and hug you right now!"
No sooner than the words could get out of my mouth, the car just seemed to slow down and I pulled

over. I had to jump out and Amy got out on cue. We met somewhere in the middle and we just hugged, jumped, and screamed. The girls woke up and saw us celebrating so we got back in the car and I just had to tell them.

"It's a secret guys." Amy said.

"It don't matter! Nobody here knows anyone at her damn job." True said.

"Girrrrrl, I'm glad I don't work there anymore. That would be hard for me to keep." It's true; it would be hard.

Amy came to America when she was fifteen years old on a track and field school trip to represent her island. She was the top sprinter from Trinidad and won all the races for her high school island-wide. She was the top runner in her age group in the 200 and the 400 meter, and the next big thing was to represent at the Penn relays. She always talked about wanting more for herself and proving to her mother that all the sacrifices she made were not in vain. After Amy won all her races at the Penn relays, her teammates and the US team went out to dinner. The two coaches talked all through the dinner to themselves and then Amy's coach told her that she had a great opportunity to stay in the US and run as a part of a high school track team. He said this would be her big break, because eventually she was going to earn big money. Coach promised her that she would be well taken care of and he would make sure that her parents were also taken care of. The next thing she knew, she was living in a New York suburb. Amy hadn't been back home to Trinidad since.

She was so proud of herself for making the decision to stay in the US, but she worried daily about her mother. Amy lived with the track coach and his family and went to high school. She continued to win race after race with her track team, but then there were bureaucratic snafus that prevented her from moving forward in the track world. She needed more and more paperwork to prove that she was an exchange student.

Eventually Amy got a job as a secretary at the hospital's clinic. When she learned that the medical assistants were paid $5.00 more than the secretaries, she went back to school and became a medical assistant. I always admired her because she kept pushing herself. She never settled; always wanting to be better.

We made it over the Chesapeake Bridge as it extended from an extraverted bold and strong character, to an underwater introvert that seemed to waver in its existence. Soon we were pulled up in front of a sun kissed yellow Victorian house.

It was now 2 o'clock in the morning and we were finally at my best friend Kelly's house in beautiful Virginia Beach. I parked directly in front of the house. The lights were blazing around the exterior of the house and her low cut grass and the SUV reflected in the mirrored double doors. She flung the doors open and ran outside to meet us. We enthusiastically greeted her.

When we entered Kelly's house her whimsical duffle bag was at the foot of a spiral staircase, which sat beside her sitting room. Her home was a combination of southern traditional and a modern kind of gem. The sitting area boasted a voluptuous white fluffy sofa with

SE-LAH; WHEN MOMMY LEFT FOR FARIN

bright turquoise throw pillows neatly placed in each corner. Complementing the throw pillows were turquoise candles on the pewter candlestick that sat on top of a wooden center table. The windows were covered with a pale yellow drape that matched perfectly with the lampshades on each end table. Beside the end tables were two wingback chairs covered in a black and white playful bird and branch fabric. Everything in Kelly's house was neat and organized. She wouldn't have it any other way.

We all took turns using the bathroom and grabbing our corned-beef sandwiches that Kelly made with the most perfect Jamaican hard-dough bread. On the white and black speckled granite counter by the matching sets of canary yellow canisters was a pitcher of homemade lemonade juice.

"Bwoy dis nice mum, gimme likkle tups more a di juice deh." I said.

"O ya mean, di driva affi good. Yu want more sandwich to?" Kelly laughed.

Kelly found a spot in the trunk of the SUV and neatly loaded her duffle bag. We hopped back in the truck and drove for two more hours to our weekend retreat. My phone was set to the Pandora music station. It was booming old dancehall tunes from the great Super Cat, "Ghetto Red Hot"; Chaka Demus and Pliers, "What a Bam Bam" and "Murder She Wrote." When we stopped for gas Shabba Ranks' melodious baritone was beating out, "GAL YU GOOD, GAL YU GOOD, GAL YU GOOD, GAL YU GOOD, OHHHH!"

We all took turns dancing in front of the truck pretending the headlights were our stage lights or we were on the soul train line. Everybody did her best "gyal yu good oh" wine. You couldn't tell us shit, especially Rain as she raised her hands in the air and did her "one wine". Then Shabba Ranks went right into *X-Rated!* "Who Say Dat Woman Can Dun?"

My Trinidadian friends got excited and simultaneously flipped upside down on the wall like they choreographed this dance. They started to wine and gyrate and "Tick Tock". They killed it. I was very much surprised that as thick as Joy's body was, she was able to do that dance so effortlessly. Youth. We high-fived each other and jumped up and down like toddlers. "Unbelievable!" I screamed. You should've seen the faces of the customers at the gas station. They were shocked pale. In the middle of the morning, they were getting an exotic dance show at the gas station. *Murder!*

Finally, we made it to North Carolina, and the place looked like a scene out of the eighties TV series "Dallas". All the homes in the neighborhood were enormous, with beautiful architecture and well-designed, well-groomed landscapes. It was dark outside, but the beauty was very clear nonetheless. As we drove down the velvety black winding road looking in disbelief as if we just wound up in wonderland. We saw a well-lit property. The house fit the description, and the address that we were looking for was mounted on the wrought iron double gate.

"Are you sure? Oh my God, look at the address again and make sure it matches. This is too awesome." I said.

"Yup ladies! This is it! We have arrived," Kelly announced.

We had the biggest mansion on the block. I turned in slowly and pulled up to the gate. On the left of the gate post was an intercom. I wanted to press the black button and announce our arrival like we were instructed to, but the splendor and beauty of the entrance held me captive for an instant. The gate was jet black with intricate curves throughout and well placed capital W's mounted at the top of the pillars. There were gilded crests in the center of the gate which stood out in beautiful contrast to the deep black of the metal that surrounded it. The dark of the night made the emblem look mystical.

Someone nudged me and as I snapped out of my awe, I turned around to see all the girls in the back of the truck. I could see that they too couldn't believe what we were all seeing. We all silently screamed with our eyes wide open. True broke the weird silence saying, "If the gate looks like this, then what the hell the inside look like?" We looked at each other and our faces looked so curious. It was still in the middle of the night or early morning, and we didn't want to get thrown out of the neighborhood, so we didn't scream. This must be a dream, I thought.

"Oh my God, is this where we're staying?" Somebody whispered.

That's what we were all thinking. Is this really where we were going to be spending the weekend? I couldn't help it anymore and I silently mouthed a scream, "OHHH MYYYY GODDDD!" The girls joined in and silently screamed too.

"Yes this is the house." Kelly said in a singing tone. "I told y'all it was a beautiful home."

"Girl, you ain't said nothing 'bout a mansion. I would have gone out and got me some Louboutins for this!" Rachelle declared matter-a-factly with the church finger. In the same instance, I eagerly pressed the intercom button and someone quickly answered. "Welcome." The voice said and the gates slowly parted.

We cautiously, but excitedly pulled in the driveway. The doors to the garage opened quietly like someone was watching us and knew the exact second we pulled up. There, sitting pretty in all her glory, was a white Maybach s600 with red interior. We were indeed in heaven; at least for the weekend. True was now drooling. She was a car freak and this car was giving her an orgasm. I could tell.

Once we got out of the car, we entered the foyer and someone who spoke with a southern accent greeted us. We were told to leave our luggage in the hall and that they would be taking us to our rooms. My sister Rory, who had flown in from Wisconsin to meet us, was seated in the golden brown and tan velvet settee smiling widely. She glided towards us with her red wine held high. "Hi y'all! Are we living it up this weekend or what?"

The woman with the southern accent was of brown complexion and possessed a real woman's body. She had envious curves in all the right places. She introduced herself as Eleanor, the governess of the house, and told us she would be taking care of us over the weekend. We followed her for a tour of the bedrooms. According to Eleanor, the family was away for the weekend but they would be joining us for breakfast on Sunday.

We toured the house and all of its splendor. Everywhere was filled with beauty. The great room with the fireplace seemed the most inviting place to be. It was March, but the fire place was jovial with a flickering blue and orange fire flame.

We didn't have to, but we decided to room together for the weekend and not get lost in the huge house forgetting the purpose in which we came; to spend time together and bond. To stay true to our purpose, we decided to room with the persons we had spent the least amount of time with.

The house had fifteen bedrooms. True, Tasha, and I picked the blue room which had a magical aura. The walls were a rich turquoise color. In the middle of the room sat a king size bed that floated like a giant cloud or pillow, covered with a striking red silk bedding. Golden drapes hung around the bed from the ceiling, they were tied in the middle to create four big knots around the bed. A Tiffany Blue Persian rug was spread out in front of it. On one side of the room sat a fireplace with a giant golden fortune cookie, on the other, a mustard chaise seated on a magic Persian rug; a great place for me to sleep.

My sister Rachelle and my friend Amy picked the golden room which had more traditional décor. My best friend Kelly and my other sister Rory picked the platinum room, where all things were pewter looking or glittered (including the Arabian inspired decorated walls and silver sequin bedspread). This room had a beautiful patio attached, which made it feel even more royal. My friend Joy and my sister Rain picked the cherry blossom decorated room. It had matching twin four post canopy beds and was whimsically decorated; suitable for young girls.

The estate declared its glory with the breaking of the daylight and we enjoyed the view. As we basked in its beauty, seated on a patio overlooking the brook, we ate Jamaican breakfast cuisine: stylish fried dumplings, ackee and saltfish, mackerel rundun, callaloo steamed with tomatoes, garlic, scallions, onions and thyme, tasty saltfish fritters, generous slices of ripe plantains, mint and original cocoa tea, and delicious cornmeal porridge. I couldn't believe my mouth; the food tasted authentic and delicious. I had to ask Eleanor if the chef was Jamaican. "We have two this weekend. One chef is Jamaican and was trained in France, and the other is from right here in North Carolina, both Cordon Bleu trained. I felt grateful and honored to be in this place and in this time for many reasons, but especially because a black family called this beautiful place home.

As we ate, we made plans for the day. Eleanor told us that we have tickets to the Asheville symphony for 6:00 pm and dinner will be served after the show at the mansion. Joy wanting to give a toast to her best friend Amy, the newlywed, stood up, adjusted her silk robe comfortably on her shoulders, picked up her mimosa and stood beside her chair. She raised her hand and her face, and eloquently honored her friend in her sweet Trinidadian accent.

"Amy, you make me proud and I think it's fitting for you to announce your marriage on this beautiful weekend. I knew when Amy fell in love. She told me about her first date and asked me not to say anything to anyone. Then she told me of another date and then another. I said, bwoy dis ting getting serious! One day I met up with Amy to go to Costco so she could use my card. You all may not know her struggle with acne, but when I look on she face, I see di gyal face look smooth like butter. I say but wait, someting inna someting. So I ask she, 'Gyal yu give up di pum pum?' She face tun red and she couldn't keep a straight face. I say 'gyal, now you can dash weh all di acne soap and face wash and all di salicylic acid you have, cause you find a good skin cleanser.' Dat is why di gyal married di white bwoy, him clear up she acne. Cheers to mi fren, you deserve love and happiness."

We all laughed and Amy confirmed she found a good thing. Eleanor got excited when she heard of Amy's nuptials and she told us secretly that she was going to plan a bachelorette party for her Saturday night, and for us to get gifts from the nearby mall.

The mall looked like any other mall. The stores' names were different; Dillard's instead of Macy's, but the merchandise were the same. The plan was to secretly buy gifts for Amy for the party. Distracting her was a piece of cake. We entered the mall through a department store that was having a one hour spa special and she needed no convincing. She heard facial and full body massage and she just opted right in. We had one hour to shop while Amy was being pampered.

By the time we got back to the mansion, the rush to get dressed for the Asheville symphony was real. We were told to be ready by 5 p.m. and at first it seemed like we had all day to get ready. However 4:40 p.m. rolled around sooner than we thought and my friggin eyelashes wouldn't stay on. Frantically, I turned on the air hoping to cool the room. I was excited about the fireplace and wanted to fully experience the luxury of the room, so I started it last night and it had been on all day. The room was too warm now and my mink eyelashes wouldn't stay on. *Great!*

I had no time to waste, so I swiveled my body into my fuchsia Herve Leger bandage dress, slipped on my black heels and tilted my head back directly under the vents of the central air hoping to cool my face, set my makeup, and help my eyelashes to stick. There was a limousine waiting outside to take all nine of us to see the orchestra, but Tasha couldn't find her shoes so we took that as an opportunity to take selfies and have a mini photo shoot for pictures for our Instagram. True was on her last pose, the signature backshot/hair flip combo, when suddenly Tasha came running out the front doors with her ugly boots raised high in her hands. "Got it!" she said with her broad smile. True and Rain fell out laughing.

"HELL NO Tasha!" True screamed.

"You gotta wear nice shoes with that dress."

"These are nice, matter of fact they are kind to me and my feet, I love them for that." Everyone else laughed and piled into the limo.

I was moved to see the orchestra filled with Blacks and minorities. Wayne Marshall, the conductor was excellent at his job; the sounds that came from the orchestra were beautiful, airy, and magical. Then it got unbelievably better. Brother Gareth Johnson was a total surprise. His command of the stage and his effortless resonance with the violin left us in awe.

None of us had any clue that sounds so sweet could come from a violin. The brother was fine and his music was divine. His youth, beauty, and eloquent hands intensified his passion and captivated the audience.

Our little crew started his standing ovation as we hopped out of our seats clapping at the end of his performance. The entire audience, that also gave him a standing ovation, was equally mesmerized. "Bravo! Bravo! Bravo!" I called out and the audience joined in. "Bravo! Bravo! Bravo!" They echoed, twas an excellent show.

After the show, while we were busy taking pictures for our social media pages in the grand theater, Rain interjected that there was a feature on her new camera that allowed her to edit and upload pictures directly from the camera to her Facebook page. She wanted us to get a group picture so she could try it. She jokingly asked a handsome stranger to oblige us and take our pictures and he willingly did.

After our mini photo session, the stranger shared that he was a photographer by trade and it was his pleasure to have so many beautiful women as his subjects. He liked our lightweight camera with the high speed shoot feature. Rain quickly chimed in that it was her camera and walked off with the tall, dark, and bearded handsome guy. For the next fifteen minutes, while at the concession stand, she was giggling and blushing with the photographer.

Back in the car, Rain was busy texting. Joy said to Rain, "Gyal a see you work dat tube top jumper tonight, da man ain't want ya leave tall."

"Did you give him your number?" Rachelle asked with both curiosity and concern.

"He wouldn't leave without it." Rain said as she smirked and held up her phone to show the screen.

Everyone took turns teasing Rain until we made it back to the mansion. A rich aromatic scent, laden with a variety of spices, welcomed us. I couldn't resist following the smell, so I tilted my nose in the air, and as I inhaled walked towards the dining room. The table was a splendor. I previewed the menu that boasted a Mediterranean delight. It read: roasted beets marinated with olive oil and red wine vinegar, baby eggplants stuffed with caramelized onions topped with feta cheese, seared peppercorn crusted yellow-fin tuna with a Mediterranean chutney, Portobello mushrooms, roasted red peppers, fresh mozzarella and pesto, grilled salmon with grazed string beans and potatoes, and breaded veal cutlets served with mushroom sauce. The table was brimmed with focaccia bread sparkling water and medium red Merlot. The spread looked so inviting that we hurriedly washed our hands at the powder room on the main floor and sat down ready to devour the rich looking meal. We ate the delectable dinner as we recapped the night over medium red Merlot.

After dinner we were hurried to the basement where there was a twelve seater movie cinema, fully outfitted with both a popcorn machine, and a candy stand with a variety of choices. We settled down to pick a movie. Kelly suggested *"The Help"* with Viola Davis, but Amy and Rory insisted that we see *"The Book of Eli"*. Rory gave it a raving review as she held her wine glass and scrolled through the choices.

We unanimously decided anything with Denzel Washington was well worth it. We had popcorn, candy, and drinks in hand. As soon as the movie started an alarm sounded. The young maid Shirley came and ushered us upstairs saying the machines hadn't been used for a while and one of them started to spark a fire, so she called the fire department. Kelly got very anxious because this was her friend's home and she did not want anything going wrong. Although we were all edgy and we wanted to wait outside, Eleanor and Shirley insisted that we stay inside because they had already unplugged all of the machines in the basement.

Eleanor answered the door when the doorbell rang. Four firefighters dressed in full gear including helmets and sledge hammers entered. I almost fainted at the thought of them ripping this beautiful home apart. "We heard there were some very hot girls in this house who started a fire, which one of you just got married?"

"Oh my goodness, what's going on?" Amy asked.

I was clueless and everyone else looked just as clueless, but then I remembered that the Governess had mentioned a Bachelorette party for Amy.

Eleanor took Amy's hand, walked her into the great room with the fireplace and sat her down on a wingback chair. With all the panic we had walked right by the room not realizing it was set up for a party. The room had a table full of erotic toys and nicely wrapped gift boxes. There was a woman waiting in the room by the table. The firefighters followed in with music and they started to dance for Amy who was seated in the wingback chair. She was hiding her face and shaking her head from side to side. "Oh my Gosh", she screamed as she peaked through the palms of her hands. The laughter and screams were a delight to Eleanor and she smiled and left us fawning over the toys and the boys.

As we watched, the dancers took off their uniforms in rhythmic motions and leaped around gyrating their hips to dance music. With their shirtless suspender clad bodies, they began a dance routine of swinging their hips, sliding one knee on the floor and standing on their hands flicking their feet in air. Their strength and flexibility were incredible and we screamed with glee.

They began to engage the rest of us. As they moved towards Rory who was already standing far off, she ran and hid with wine still in hand peeking out from behind the wall. One dancer flipped Rain off her chair and onto his chest holding her with one hand as he brought her up and down his body. Rachelle held her head back and started to fan. A dancer quickly danced over to her, put his hand around her throat and rocked her back and forth. We screamed louder with surprise. Another dove onto the floor and slithered towards Joy's thick body. He pushed her legs open and nestled his head between her legs. Joy flung her head back and covered her face with one hand. Simultaneously, the dancer flipped his body up in the chair and threw his legs across my lap as he rolled his body like a snake onto mine. My eyes and everyone else's popped wide open at his flexibility. We threw dollar bills all over them. Amy was not shy anymore. She moved to the instruction of the dancer, standing with her legs wide open and head towards the floor as he pumped his body on hers. Kelly screamed and pushed back at one as he tried to pick her up. He realized her resistance, slapped her on the ass and turned her around to her chair.

Tasha was enjoying the show until a dancer picked her up from behind and dropped his body on the floor with her on top of him. She shockingly sprang to her feet while the money she held in her hands spewed all over the place. One dancer took True's hand as she sat in the sofa and marched her to the middle of the room. He then laid her on the floor used one finger to draw an imaginary line from her mouth to her toes without ever touching her. She seemed tantalized and her eyes gazed quickly back and forth as she waited to see what would be his next move. He laid his body vertically next to hers with his head to her feet. He then licked her toes with his tongue. We all screamed in disbelief and euphoria as we filled the house with music, screams, and cheering. By the time the dancers left we had been worked into a frenzy.

Shoshanna, the heavy-breasted, tiny waisted, big booty woman by the exotic toys table introduced herself as a sex toy educator. She proceeded to give us some knowledge on the weird looking toys. Our thirst for sex toy education must have increased by the salacious dancing and Shoshanna was definitely knowledgeable enough to quench it. She seemed to know all the sex toys in the world and everything about them. We gobbled up toys and instructions and oils and candy and all things sex related, including the coveted "butterfly" which Rain promised would give us continuous orgasms.

"Girrrrl, my butterfly is my best friend," she announced as she gave her wink of approval. Rain highly recommended it and Shoshanna concurred. Amy's excitement was uncontainable as she opened her gifts she kept asking, "When did you guys plan this?"

True gave her a pair of red furry handcuffs. Rachelle gave her a pink diary to document her joyous moments. "Anytime you have a quarrel, just reach for this book and read as much of the joyous moments it takes for you to see beyond your misunderstanding. I call it 'a dose of encouragement'."

Rory, after hiding from the dancing firefighters and the sex toy education, came out with her gift. She gave Amy a set of monogrammed champagne glasses. "Nothing a good glass of wine can't fix!" She declared.

"OMG, where did you find this?!" Amy screamed.

Who would have guessed that Rain was poetic? Her gift was a poem strategically teaching how to give "super" head?! No lies, I was floored. Kelly bought Amy a recipe book titled, *"The Way to a Man's Heart is Through His Stomach"*. Joy's gift was a set of Kegel balls to help her strengthen her vaginal muscles. Tasha gave her a pair of black furry high heeled bedroom slippers, (which we were all surprised to see).

"Tasha, what you know about those heels?" True asked.

"Cause you know damn well you don't wear nothing else but those damn ugly ass boots. Tasha, do you wear them with your negligee?" Tasha rolled her eyes and said nothing in response.

My gift to Amy was a gorgeous white French lace lingerie piece. "This is the prettiest thing eeh?" She declared.

In between opening every gift, Amy kept on repeating, "Y'all are the fucking best, I swear."

Rory passed out more wine and we giggled and danced through the night. The house was full with laughter and excitement.

***

The morning after a party is usually the worst. I rolled out of the golden chaise crawling to the toilet. As I got sicker I heard someone ask, "You okay?" It was True. She was the first to curse you out, but was also the first to check on you; always.

"Let me tell Eleanor you up here dying." She glanced over at me and then waltzed over to the phone. Within five minutes the governess was there with Tylenol and orange juice. "Here, take this." She said as she handed me the glass of rich yellow orange juice. "Lie down on your side for about twenty minutes my dear. You'll start to feel better soon. Once you feel better, come downstairs for breakfast. You will definitely feel better after you eat breakfast. Eleanor stopped before leaving out of the room, giving me time to get myself together. "The Wallace's are back from their trip. They will be going to church with you this morning. You'll be leaving at ten, so you have an hour which is plenty of time to feel much better. I'll check on you in a few minutes." I took the Tylenol and the orange juice and closed my eyes as I laid on the cold granite bathroom floor. I inhaled deeply, ignoring the pounding sound in my head and fell asleep.

It must have been about five minutes later, at least it felt like it, when the governess came back to check if I were still alive. "How are you feeling?" She asked as she kneeled over me and helped me off the floor.

"Not good. I don't feel nauseated anymore, but my head still hurts."

"Your sister Rory also has a headache. She doesn't think she'll make it to church."

Rory might have had an entire bottle or two of wine last night, so I could understand her having a headache and feeling nauseated. I only had two glasses however, so why did I feel like my head was a jug of water and the light was a laser beam aiming to eradicate my sight?

"You need some more sleep, I'll be back to get you in twenty minutes."

Twenty minutes passed and Eleanor came back to help me dress. By now, I felt much better and the headache was gone. When I descended the winding staircase wearing my sunglasses, I was thrilled to find the family still at the table with the rest of my girls, including Rory. I greeted Mrs. Wallace, her husband, and their teenage son Rokk.

Breakfast was what the doctor ordered for my hangover. The menu read Persian Fusion: an array of jams, fruits, flatbreads, fresh nuts, beef, lamb, pomegranate chicken, and Persian potato and cucumber salad. The coffee was invigorating.

"Sorry we couldn't be here to welcome you on Friday night." Mrs. Wallace started, "Rokk here created a robot that could play basketball for his high school science project. The thing got picked to be part of a fundraiser playoff game for Tomorrow's Builders High School, an inner city high school in East St. Louis, Illinois. It was amazing! I'm so glad we were a part of this event. The school is one of the least resourced schools in America."

"What do you mean? Are they very poor, or just missing a few resources like after school activities?" Rachelle asked.

"They are extremely poor, so the idea of bringing different robots from around the country there to play basketball created some attention that they truly needed."

"Okay," Amy nodded.

"In fact," Mrs. Wallance continued, "It created a media mania and people from all over the science and tech world were there."

"Nice! Was any money donated to the school over the weekend?" Kelly asked.

"Yes of course. It was awesome! They were exchanging ideas and brainstorming more ways to bring funds and other resources to the school, and potentially giving these students the help they need to succeed." Mrs. Wallace said passionately. "...and most importantly, hope. They brought hope to the students and the community." She added.

Everyone at the table had something sensible to interject but me. I nodded in agreement of Mrs. Wallace and unintentionally added "this coffee is so good". I couldn't believe that was my comment after such an interesting and impactful conversation. Instead of scolding me, Mr. Wallace jumped to my rescue and declared that a friend of his was starting a new coffee company and had sent it over for him to try.

"It's called Jablum. I love it too, but I will certainly let him know that it's so good that you couldn't stop thinking about it," He laughed.

"You do that and I'll do one better. I'll write a review!" I declared.

The Wallace's were a Jamaican couple who owned one of the world's largest software-education company. Mrs. Wallace and Kelly had been friends since they attended Excelsior High School in Jamaica.

"So how you ladies like the fire fighters last night?" Mrs. Wallace asked.

"Aaaah, you knew about that?" Kelly asked with her eyes wide open.

"Of course I knew. I suggested it and came up with the fire in the basement!" Mrs. Wallace boasted.

"It was truly intoxicating. I don't think any one of us would have come up with such a perfect scenario. It was an unbelievable night, even down to the popcorn machine sparking fire. You're good Mrs. Wallace!" Rachelle said.

"Girl, call me Peaches."

After breakfast, we headed to church in our fancy dresses and fascinators, being chauffeured in limousines like royalty. Church was a "bring down the Holy Ghost" kind of worship. The praise and worship team should get a record deal if record deals still exist; and that pastor? He brought the Word! They called us to the altar for prayer and I never miss the opportunity for prayer.

While we were standing at the altar waiting for our individual prayers, I noticed that each time the pastor touched the forehead of a prayer seeker, the person would fall to the floor. I knew that would never happen to me, but I kept wondering what was going on.

However, what happened next was totally unexpected and surreal for me. The pastor touched me one time while he was praying for me and I fell to the floor convulsing. Yes, there I was in a strange church, sprawled out on the floor convulsing uncontrollably. I never lie. I made a mental note when it was all over that the next time I'm a guest at a church I will keep my ass seated.

After church we changed into comfortable clothes and went out for a two hour drive to the Charlotte South Park Mall. So we could all ride together, we traveled in a Sprinter Mercedes Benz bus. Of course Tasha couldn't find her shoes and Kelly, Rachelle, and Rain were the first ones in the bus. I made it in before the Wallace's and the Trinidadians. True was late, but Tasha was last. This time she was already wearing her boot. We were all surprised.

At the mall we were just glad to get out of the truck and stroll around. However, we quickly learned rich people don't shop like that. As if our weekend wasn't already ethereal, we were greeted by a concierge who escorted us directly to the Versace store. I do recall, while on the bus, hearing Mr. Wallace say that store would be his first stop as the mall closes early on Sundays. Peaches didn't bat an eye. She had the same jovial smile as she did all day. It sounded logical to me, but when we got into the store, I was amazed. Peaches told us to look around and choose something we really loved. "Pick up anything you like." Peaches was busy saying. "I'm not getting anything today, but whatever you like let Christian know."

Christian was Mrs. Wallace's concierge. He walked with a bounce and on his tippy toes like a ballerina as he gently swayed his hips and whisked us off. As Christian led us into a back room, Peaches remained out front, being distracted by another personal shopper. In the back room there were more people, which I quickly learned were the Wallace's' family and friends. Mr. Wallace explained that it was his wife's birthday today and she begged him not to make a big deal. So, he planned a secret shopping spree and party at her favorite store. We were handed strawberry filled champagne and giant shrimp kabobs.

Soon after we arrived to the back room, Peaches was ushered in and as she walked in her mouth dropped wide open. She had a super puzzled look on her face. We all yelled, "Surprise!" Immediately a steel drum band started playing a 'Happy Birthday' song. It was nostalgic for me and by the look on her face, for her too. The only other time I heard that version of the song was years ago on a show called, "Ring Ding", with Ms. Louise Bennett.

"Lawd geezampeeze Wayne Wallace yu ears hard eeh!"

"You de here to?!"

"And you!"

"OMG not you! How on earth you guys keep this from me?" She whined surprisingly and joyfully.

While the music played, the personal shopper brought out racks and racks of clothing, handbags, accessories and more champagne.

"Just say yes my dear. Just say yes!" Christian repeated. "It's yours, whatever you desire."

Instead of choosing from the designers' latest, Peaches was busy trying to reach every soul in the room. Her hugs were long and strong with a tight squeeze. *What a life*, I thought as I watched Peaches who a minute ago had everything in the world, become overwhelmed with her favorite people in the world. I admired the passion in her eyes as she looked at everyone. We nine, just some regular girls from around the way, got to experience it all. I truly didn't feel like choosing anything. I just wanted to bask in the moment of what was really important; family, good friends, and love. I was no fool though. I was not going to pass up Christian's suggestion of a baby blue cinched waist hooded silk blazer and pencil pants with an encrusted crystal corset. Divine.

"Great taste," Christian complemented. That is from the new spring collection. It's brand new too! You will be first to have that at any party this year."

***

Monday was our last day in North Carolina, and we planned to have a relaxing day. As we packed our bags, we were all hoping and praying Tasha would know where the hell her other boot was when we were ready to leave. Peaches told us that she had a friend who was a spiritual healer coming to have breakfast with us. We all dressed up for breakfast with the guest. The drawing room was decorated with multi-colored gift bags seated on the desk. I counted ten. The breakfast smelled really great, so I smiled at the gift bags and did the greedy girl dance over to the dining room as I glanced over my shoulder trying to see which gift bag was mine.

I noticed that Mr. Wallace, Rokk, and Peaches were not at the dining table. As soon as I sat down though, Peaches came in with her irresistible bubbly smile, wearing a monochromatic matted purple pant suit.

She looked stylishly dressed for work, but her smile said she was meeting with her friends. Before she sat down she sang, "Morninnnnng!" while gesturing to all of us. Then she hugged her friend and gave her a warm introduction.

"This is my friend Eva and she is a spiritual therapist. She has been an instrumental key to my sanity and I'm so excited to share her with you today, because I know you will be blessed after hearing her story and some of her theories of life."

"Happy belated birthday," Eva said as they hugged and kissed both sides of their cheeks. "It's nice to be here. I just came in from Rwanda on Saturday afternoon and I was exhausted all day yesterday. I slept right through the birthday party. I'm so sorry I missed the surprise, but I knew I was going to see you today and this special group of women that you've been talking about." Eva turned to look at us. "How have you ladies been enjoying your weekend getaway?"

We were all excited to recap the weekend and we unanimously agreed that although the entire weekend was extraordinary, Sunday was a surreal day. From the Holy Ghost throwing people down in church, to the private Versace shopping experience, everything was just totally unbelievable. None of us had ever experienced anything like that.

"That's Peaches' church honey. You'd better be ready when you go up in there; it's a holy-ghost filled battle." Eva said as she swung her traditional locs from her back to one side of her shoulder. Eva had a heart shaped face with bold hazel eyes and a sporty body type. She wasn't slim, but because she was tall and her body parts were toned and well proportioned, at first glance she appeared that way. She was wearing a white buttoned down shirt tucked into her white pants and metallic accessories. "So ladies I would like to begin by telling you a little bit about myself."

"Wait, wait." Peaches raised her hands to stop her friend from continuing.

"This is my friend Kelly, and these are her friends. Let her introduce them before you begin." Peaches said.

"Oh my goodness," Kelly said as she stood, rested her hands on top of her full breasts. "I just want to take this moment to say a personal thank you to my friend Peaches. Thank you and your family for opening your doors and your hearts to me and my friends. I mean, this weekend was beyond our wildest dreams. You told me that you would take care of everything. 'Just come K, just come.' She said you don't have to worry about a thing; and I mean the level of attention to detail that you put into everything has been beyond elaborate. The international food menus that we were presented with for each meal, your governess and the warm team who catered to our every need, the trip to the symphony with that orchestra, the surprise bachelorette party, oh my goodness and then your husband with that surprise birthday party, just awesome, simply awesome! Thank you for everything!"

"I love you Kelly." Peaches said with a smile.

Kelly turned to her left and waved her hand as if she were pushing the air in front of her bosom. "This is my friend Rachelle, she is the sister of my sister-in-law Rashae. Next to her is True, my sister-in-law's cousin. She is a true friend, always there when you need her and especially to curse someone out. Next to True is Rain; my sister-in-law's sister. Next to Rain is Amy the newlywed. She is a friend of Rashae. Next to Amy is Joy. She is also my sister-in-law's friend. Next to Joy is my sister-in-law Rashae, and Tasha who is seated on her left," she continued gesturing to towards Rashae and Tasha, "She is my brother's wife. Seated next to Tasha is Rory. She is also my sister-in-law Rashae's sister. On behalf of all of us, thank you Peaches!"

Eva smiled and said, "You all remind me of a big family, full of sisters. What does this group mean to each of you?"

We each took turns saying mushy stuff about what the group meant to us as we ate Belgian waffles with fresh fruit toppings and sipped Jablum coffee. Eva loved it, as evident by her smile and her nods. With a soft maneuver of her light brown locs, she said, "I love it and

51

I love that our paths cross. I planned to be in Rwanda at this time, more than a year ago. In January when I called Peaches to remind her that I was going on a long trip, she was like, 'Wow! I can't believe you won't be here to meet my friend Kelly and her amazing girl group who are doing some important work in bonding and healing themselves.' So I said no I won't, but I'll be back the day before your fiftieth birthday. This woman got so excited. I thought she was happy that I'd be back for some elaborate party she was planning to celebrate her fiftieth; but no, she was more excited because this is the weekend you all had planned to be here. She said she wouldn't be planning anything for her birthday. For her birthday, she wanted to give more of herself and she planned to give you her time and attention."

"Now if you know Peaches, you know that she gives to more organizations than the Red Cross."

"Yes!" Kelly declared.

"I say that to say, the Divine knows our unfulfilled spiritual needs and he will always align the universe to nurture it." I could see the sincerity and passion in Eva's body. Her voice was smooth as honey, yet very prominent and powerful. She moved me. She held up the good ole church finger and said, "Now, I have been going to trips like the one I went to in Rwanda for over thirty years. My first trip was when I went to Villavicencio in central Colombia while I was in medical school. A friend of mine was going with her parents who were plastic surgeons. She knew she would be the only teenager from America and she didn't want to go by herself. I had a mandatory must leave campus for the upcoming Thanksgiving holiday, so her family

52

sponsored me. The people we helped were so grateful that it made a lasting impression on me and I vowed to go as often as I could; which has been every year for the past thirty years."

"Wow! That sounds so rewarding." I exclaimed, eagerly waiting for her to continue.

"It was," Eva resumed, "My decision to become a plastic surgeon was made on that very first trip to Colombia, South America. I saw how repairing cleft lip and cleft palate changed both the individuals getting the repair and the family's spirit. I learned on that medical trip, that giving of self to others is one of the most powerful medicines in the world. If you learn to give selflessly with no regrets, you can heal from anything." We all nodded in agreement.

By this time the maids were clearing the table and giving us room to get comfortable. Eva took a seat and started motioning for us to gather and listen intently. "My disease," Eva continued, "was holding on to hate and resentment. When I was a teenager I was brutally hurt by the man who was my father. I was an only child for my mother, and my mother was also an only child. My mother, my grandmother, and I all lived in a little house with one room and a kitchen in a town called Mountain Brook in Birmingham, Alabama. My father was the town's drunk and he was a white man. One day my mother sent me to get some package his mother had promised her. I remember it like it was yesterday." She said with a grimace.

***

53

"Eva, Eva!"

"Yes, Momma?"

"Walk ova to Mrs. Davis' house and collect that package she left for you."

I had just finished packing my bag for the one hundredth time. It was handmade by my grandma, just for me. I gently lifted the bag from the bed and tucked it neatly in the corner behind the bed. Then, I went outside to my mother. She was over a wash tub and when I went over to her she stopped, looked up at me, and smiled.

My momma was very proud of me. I was the only kid in the neighborhood that knew how to read very well. I was also the brightest kid in my school and I'm sure I was the only person in town my age to go away to college. So, my momma either smiled at me or gave me a kiss almost every time I came into her presence. She was very bright herself and my grandmother thought she was going to be a teacher and have a respectful life. Instead my mother got pregnant by a white drunk with me.

When I was born in April 1963, it was in the heat of segregation and the Civil Rights Movement. My father and his family denied that I was his, but secretly his mother would stop by and give me small parcels every so often. When my father was drunk he would also bring things over for me, but because he was always so belligerent when he came over, my grandma stopped him from coming altogether. It was always just my grandma, momma, and me. Those ladies poured everything they had in me.

My mother woke up every morning, hours before school and gave me a two hour lesson on geography, science, and English literature. I mumbled about getting up extra early to study and then going to school. We had no electric light, but my momma would light the lamp by our only other furniture besides the bed, which was a table pushed up to the wall and three chairs pushed under the table. We left grandma in the bed, then momma pulled out the books from underneath the bed and we sat at the table and studied until it was time for me to get ready for school. Momma got my books from a woman she washed clothes for, Mrs. Okere, whose husband was head of the steel workers on the railroads.

On weekends all three of us walked to the market on Saturday mornings, and went to church on Sundays. We stayed all day in church, visited the sick and shut in, or did other church activities.

By the time I got to first grade the teachers noticed that I knew a lot and they encouraged me. I skipped second grade and fourth grade, and by the time I was nine, I finished grade school. The day when I was going away to college I was only but fourteen years old.

"So when the word got out that I was going away to Miles College, my father and his mother left word with Mrs. Okere that they had a package they were going to give me."

Eva crossed her fingers and looked down at the marvelous table, exposing her reflection. She was a

55

strong woman with defined cheekbones and proper posture.

On the day before I left for college, my mother called me and told me to go get the package, because we were leaving early the next morning." Eva began to fidget with her fingers. "It was the worst day of my life." She began again. "My father and his mother lived a stone throw away from me. In fact you could see straight into their house from mine. I left my mother outside washing some clothes and my grandma walked me to the front where she could see me walk over there. As I got closer I called out for Mrs. Davis. I didn't see her, but I saw Lanny, my father. He walked up to the front rooms door with a towel drying his hand. He leaned against the post of the door and watched me walk to the gate.

"Is Ms. Davis there?" I asked.

"No."

"Okay," I said and turned to walk away.

"She left something for ya, come get it." He motioned me to come in with his head as he continued to wipe his hands in the towel.

I looked back at my grandmother still watching from the gate, and then I walked into the yard and up the steps to their front porch. When I got up on the porch, Lanny turned and walked into the house. I followed. They had a big red sofa in the middle of their front room and a huge dining table in the back of the room not too far from the sofa. On the table just behind the sofa was a small box. As I walked to the table, Lanny walked towards me and we both got to the table at the same time. I put my hands out to reach for the box and Lanny leaned into me and pressed my body up on the table with his. I froze. I don't remember thinking anything, but when I felt his hardness on me and then his wetness I said, "Lanny, my grandma is waiting at the gate for me to get back."

As he eased up off of me, he reached over for the box and pushed it on my chest where his wetness was on my dress. The walk back to my grandma felt like the longest ever. I kept trying to come up with something to say to her if she were to see that my dress was wet. Anyway, I kept it hidden. I changed my dress when I got inside the house and never said anything to my grandma or my mother. I just didn't want anything to stop me from going away to school. I thought if I said anything it would change everything my mom and I had been working so hard for."

"What Lanny did and my keeping that secret almost destroyed me when I went away to school. I had nightmares every night for the first year and then I had rage and was fighting with everyone; and then there was depression. I didn't know how to deal with it all. The family I went to live with in Fairfield, Alabama were friends of my grandma, and they were sensitive about me being so young." She shook her head with a soft chuckle.

"They thought everything that was happening was directly related to me being an only child or me being away from my momma and grandma at such a young age. They loved me through it." She said reassuringly with a small smile.

When I had my nightmare, Mrs. Evans, who I was staying with, would come into my room and comfort me until I went back to sleep. One day Mrs. Evans told me that God already knew what was going on in me and He had already fixed it. But, she said to me, 'you are still holding on to whatever it is. Tell me what story plays in your head every day Eva. What do you hear when no one else is around? No matter what it is, she urged, God will forgive you. But the question is are you willing to forgive yourself and others? Do you want to live? Baby you won't ever be able to truly live your own life if you are still holding on to what should have been. Baby you gotta let go and let God."

Eva clasped her hands together and gave them a slight shake and slightly nodded her head. "That night I told Mrs. Evans what was boiling up in me and she became a good counselor. She sat at the foot of my bed and talked with me every night and then prayed with me before I fell asleep. By the time I finished college and it was time for me to go on to medical school, I felt like a new person. My rage, depression, and nightmares went away. My life's mission since has been to give back through my career and in my daily life, because that is the medicine I need to sustain a healthy being. I know every woman has a story worth telling. Here is my question to you. What story plays in your head every day? What do you hear when no one else is around?"

Rachelle's Story
Revelation

When I was a child I was broken. In December of 1975, with the intention of finding "the good life" in America, my mother left me and my four siblings in Sligoville St. Catherine, Jamaica, West Indies. I was just seven years old. I am Rachelle. I was left with my brothers and sisters Ricky, Ron, Rashae, and baby Rain.

Like so many others in that era, my mom and her sister left their children with their parents to go abroad and work. Their hope was that they and their children would have better opportunities. Immediately after my mom left, I began to feel an emptiness inside. I wandered around the house trying to become someone's daughter; not just a big sister or a cousin. My grandmother was busy running a home with about umpteen children; all ranging in ages from teenagers to a toddler. Unable to be someone's daughter, I started to feel unwanted. Most days my stomach felt like it was churning, like it feels right now." Rachelle held her belly while she spoke, as she physically fought the resurfaced feeling. She closed her eyes and continued.

While I was waiting for my mother's return, I turned eight and outgrew some of my clothes. That year, close to Christmas, my grandmother received a barrel from my mother with clothes, shoes and food. With that barrel came excitement and hope. I was excited about getting brand new pretty clothes, and hopeful that soon I would see my mother. Then I turned nine and noticed two painful little buds growing on my chest. I soon realized that I was getting older and my body was changing. A few years after my body changed, I was raped. In addition to feeling abandoned, I was further damaged by the rape and keeping it a secret. Everyone noticed that I had begun to be disrespectful, not listening to the rules, and constantly yelling or fighting my siblings and my cousins. They scolded me for acting out.

My mother left when I was a seven year old, with long skinny legs and arms; so long they touched my knees. "Rachelle, you are a big girl and a big sister. While I am away I need you to help mama and Aunty P. take care of your brothers and sisters."

"Yes mommy." I remembered smiling; glad to help.

"I am going away, but soon I will send for you all." She said with a soft and convincing voice.

"Yes mommy," I smiled.

I turned eight and mommy didn't send for me. I continued taking care of my brothers and sisters just as she said. As I grew older, I was given more responsibilities. I was sent to Spanish Town market to sell fruits and vegetables like "Chuo-cho", and to buy groceries to bring back home. One day, when I was coming home from the market, I went with a trusted cousin to his home.

As I got out of the taxi at the square, right in front of the butcher's shop, I saw him. He was wearing his tight shirt and wide leg pants and holding something in his hand wrapped in brown paper. He told me if I followed him home to drop the parcel off, he would help me take the groceries home. The bags were heavy and it was a long walk from the square to the village, so I thought it was a good idea. Once I was at his house, there was no hope for me. I remember trying to pry his tightly gripped hand from around my neck, but I don't even remember passing out. When I woke up to his voice saying, "wake up, yu haffi leave before mi fada come home", there was bright red blood where I laid, and when I stood up, the blood ran down my legs the way the sweat runs down my face when the wicked Spanish Town sun blazed so hot I wanted to die. I wiped myself with the hem of my dress. I was bleeding and bruised, and my private hurt. When I got home I thought I better not let anyone find out that I didn't come straight home. Mama was waiting for me on the veranda, so I dropped the groceries that I had on the floor next to her and ran to the toilet. I took off the soiled dress, cleaned up my private, and dropped the dress into the pit toilet.

61

I was sick for days with a roasting fever. Aunty P nursed me with garlic tea and told me funny jokes until I had the energy to smile again. I couldn't keep anything down and the fever wouldn't go away. One day Mama gave me a bath, put me in some new underwear, and took me to the neighborhood clinic. The nurse was a round white skinned lady. She wore a white dress and a funny looking hat which sat in the middle of the top of her head. She walked like a bobble head doll. Her office looked extremely clean and organized and it smelled like turpentine. It had clear glass bottles on the counters with cottons, thin square cloths, flat sticks, and shiny silver tools in them. She told me to lay across her big lap and she gave me an injection in my buttocks.

Not too long after that incident, I went to Kingston to live with an aunt. I lived with her, her husband, their three children, and her mother in-law for about two years. I was often misunderstood there, and I paid for it dearly with lots of "beatens". Later my sister Rashae came to live with us, and I found my very first friend. She listened to every word I shared, but I never had the courage to tell her what happened to me that day. She seemed too young to understand.

When I was thirteen, I left Jamaica in the middle of a rainy mysterious night, with big raindrops so loud they sounded like giant rocks as they hit the car. The heavy rain pelted my back as I tried to duck them from hitting my newly hot-pressed hair. They drenched my dark red bolero and black Chinese slippers as I ran from the curb into the shelter of the airport. By the time I dragged my suitcase into the airport I was soaking wet. Salted tears mixed with fresh rain rolled down my face and onto my new dress. I was traveling with my aunt.

"Why you upset Rachy?" She asked gently. I said nothing. Instead of answering, I bowed my head trying to hide my face. I was going to America to see my mother and I was a mess. By this time, my mother had four more children - Raven, Ryan, Rory and baby Ruby. I soon realized I was now the oldest of nine children.

I arrived in America yearning for love and attention, especially from my mom, but she was very busy with work and the life of a mother to give me all the attention I needed. I got busy helping her as much as I could. As soon as she blurted out a comment or a command I was on it, ready to help, hoping to make her happy with me.

"What a head of hair! Comb Rory's hair."

"Take Raven to the barber shop."

"Help Ryan with his homework and mek sure him bade today, today, today."

Life in America with mommy was busy, but I couldn't get into school so I kept busy helping out at home. Eventually all the papers I needed for school were straightened out and I was able to start.

School was strange in the beginning. Everyone was rushing and bumping into each other in the halls. They never even acknowledged me when they bumped me. It was like I was invisible. One day, I met a young man who noticed me. I noticed him too because he was tiny, but he had muscles and looked like a strong man. He told me he liked my smile, and that he'd been watching me for a while lugging my heavy book bag around. From that day on he kept saying kind things to me, and he carried my book bag to my class that was next to one of his. He drove his father's old red BMW and would leave school grounds at lunchtime to get cooked lunch from a Jamaican restaurant. He loved and adored me. He gave me anything I wanted; especially his time.

We spent hours talking on the telephone and when mom wasn't home, we would meet at my house. I snuck out through the fire escape and we spent time talking in his father's car until late in the night.

I knew I was falling in love. We always had fun. We had more than a great time when we were together. Laughter and music were everywhere when I was with him. The summer came and we spent almost every day together. Those summer days passed quickly, filled with basement parties, exciting romps at Rye Playland, and my favorite trip of all, a getaway to Virginia Beach; just the two of us. We sucked up colored snow cones to cool our flaming love. We walked the entire boardwalk hand in hand, kissing on each other. We couldn't get enough of dreaming and planning our future. We were going to have four children, a house, some pet fish, a red Maxima for me, and a black Infinity for him.

It wasn't long after the summer ended that things changed between me and my first love. I started to notice that he was not coming to see me at home as often as he used to. We also were not talking on the telephone as long as we did before. He seemed to be too busy to meet me in the school courtyard during my lunch period and when I went to his, he said 'that didn't look good' for me to cut class, and he urged for me to go back to class. My friends started to tell me that he had another girlfriend, but when I confronted him, he denied it. He couldn't hide it for long and I started to see for myself. My first love was a cheater. When I was around him he still made me feel special so it was hard for me to stay away from him. There were a few times we broke up and each time I swore I would never go back to him ever. This time I yelled and screamed and I threw my shoe at his head. It was over for us and I meant it.

The next summer, I became friendly with my neighbor and we started going out together. I was with him physically, but my mind was not there. He would hold my hands and rubbed the top as we walked and that irritated me. I didn't feel the butterflies in my stomach for him the way I did for my First Love. He didn't make me laugh as hard and his music was very different. However, I enjoyed that he wanted to spend time talking and listening to me. But oh, how I missed my First Love calling me.

At the end of the summer on a very hot August day, the week before going back to school and starting a new grade, my First Love began calling me again. Of course, he promised never to cheat again and I believed him, again. We were back together and I just knew things were going to be different this time. I was so excited to be back in his arms, hearing his big laugh, and his perfect music.

As I tried to like my body the way my First Love did, I noticed it was making changes. I watched as it grew. I was getting sick every morning before school and some days during school. One day I got so sick at school that my teacher sent me to the nurse's office. She then told me to follow up with my doctor. Later, I learned from my clinic visit that I was pregnant. I was scared, sad, and uncertain. I was sixteen and pregnant. How would I tell my mom?

Finally, I told a cousin who told my mother. The day my mom and I spoke was very difficult. I remembered her calling me into her room. She had an attic-style closet and I sat in the closet while she sat on her bed. I felt so afraid and she looked so upset. Once my mom and I finally spoke, we made some calculations which made me more confused than I already was. I was not sure who the father was. My mother did not want me to jump to any conclusions, and she advised me to keep whatever we discussed right where we were. She sounded so protective and I relished that feeling.

When I told my boyfriend I was pregnant he was overwhelmed with joy. He couldn't wait to share the news with all his friends and family. A beautiful, healthy baby boy was born one very cold winter's day. He came sooner than calculated, but just as expected; perfectly.

My mother and I never spoke about my uncertainty and I never mentioned it to my First Love. We jumped right into raising a bouncing baby boy who brought both us and our families so much joy. I tried hard to forget the truth, but it grew bigger every day. When I remembered the lies, I buried them deep within my bones.

Four years after reuniting with my mom, after we had begun working on our bonding, after I had finally started to trust again, and after I was just beginning to regain my smile, I lost her in a horrible car accident. My mom had left with some family members to go to her cousin's wedding. On their way back home their car was struck by a stolen vehicle. My mom died instantly. My mind, my life, and my world was truly upside-down. I felt lost and abandoned once again. There was so much that was supposed to happen at that time for both me and my mom. She was planning to go back to school to become a nurse, and she was supposed to be attending my graduation. I ended up missing my graduation.

Three of my siblings, my grandmother, and an aunt came from Jamaica to attend mom's funeral. My Aunt Rose's big house where we had been living for years, suddenly felt small as it swelled with more children and more adults and even more things to do. My mind raced all day with thoughts of what I should have said to her and what I should be saying to my First Love now. It was too late; too late for me and my mother and way too soon for me and my First Love. We would have to talk about my uncertainty another time. My mother was gone and my life was changed forever. Everything overwhelmed me, including loneliness and fear. Fearing I would lose my First Love too, I packed up all my things in some boxes and moved out of the house and in with him.

When I moved in with my boyfriend and his family, we had great times and ugly times. Periodically, he would ask me if the baby was his and for me to take a DNA test. We argued loudly and I told him boldly never to question me about our child again. He told me, "People say he doesn't look like me." I fought back to keep my family together, and he kept loving me and our baby boy.

He became my husband and we had two beautiful little girls. The arguments were less, but the doubts grew as big as an elephant and stronger than an ox. I found myself becoming very angry and bitter towards my mom and blaming her gave me some relief. I blamed her for all the pain I had ever endured in my life. I thought everything wrong was really her fault. If she had never left me, I wouldn't have endured all the pain I had suffered. My heart grew as heavy as lead and the weight made me weak. The secret I had kept within my bones began to ooze out into my bloodstream. My body could no longer endure and I became toxic. I yelled at everyone for the least of things. I was diagnosed with hypertension and my hands shook all the time. I found myself getting sick - mind, body, and soul. I knew I was dying. I had walked through the valley of darkness with a potent poison within me for too many years.

I remember locking myself in the darkness of my closet one early morning about 4 a.m., and I started crying out to God, asking Him to please shine His light on me again and heal me. I was on my knees and my hands were clasped under my chin. I shut my eyes tight and I recited all the promises of God that I could remember. My mouth was moving as fast as a windy flame, but I didn't let out a sound. "I am not a bad person! I made a mistake!" I told God. I asked him for healing and deliverance. I wanted to live; not just for me, but for my children as well. When I walked out of the darkness of the closet and into my bedroom, the rays of the sun on the horizon burst through my window pane shining strong, bold, and warm. I had no idea I had been praying for hours and a new day had come.

One day I was in church when a young guest speaker delivered a sermon about "the woman at the well". I thought that was God speaking to me and offering me a chance to be saved. God led me to therapy and one day I buckled under the unbearable truth.

In therapy, I learned so much about myself and what I was experiencing. It was so refreshing to live in my truth. I learned how important it was for me to forgive me, because God had already forgiven me. I then forgave my mom and released her. She was only a woman who wanted the best for her children. Forgiving others was initially hard and that took years of work, but the more I forgave, the lighter I felt. I was shedding the weight off my shoulders and I was coming alive. I got better every day. My ugly cocoon was gone and I had blossomed into a beautiful God-fearing woman - mistakes and all. I thanked God for his word and read it daily.

Every night I went to sleep after reading Psalms 23, because it gave me that sense of peace I needed to rest. I had learned, 'The Lord was My Shepherd, I shall not go insane.' Through therapy I felt free and healthy, but happiness eluded me. I decided it was time to tell my husband what I had known for years.

We sat down in the kitchen to have tea and to discuss the bills that were laid out on the table between us one afternoon. He drank his favorite ginger tea in his favorite cup. He had a special love for the one with the chipped handle that he refused to throw out, because King made him that for Father's Day when he was in grade school. My red cup with mint tea trembled as I raised it to my mouth. I couldn't hold it in any longer and as he said the car payment would have to go out late so we could pay the light bill, I told him.

"King is not your child."

His black skin immediately turned pale and I knew his heart stopped. The truth cut my husband like a knife and his bleeding heart flooded our entire home. He wallowed like a wild beast caught in a trap and our children cringed. His anger frightened them, but they were comforted by his familiar love. He was strong and determined to endure. His anger was harsh, but his strength was admirable and I loved him even more. He stopped speaking to me and I appreciated that, because it gave me relief that he found a way to punish me. I watched as his eyes grew too heavy to look up at King when they talked.

"Our love is an ongoing battle. Even with fractures and lesions no one wants to throw in the towel." Rachelle continued, while we all listened. "I think we are both trying to have an individual win. Our days are filled with quiet fights, loud neglects, and new disrespects.

For now, I find peace in God's promises because I know He loves me. The Psalmist says in Psalm 57:3, *'He will send help from heaven to rescue me, disgracing those who hound me. My God will send forth his unfailing love and faithfulness'*. Selah.

I have three beautiful children whom I love and adore. They and my grandchildren are the best parts of who I am and I am grateful, because I am alive and in my right mind."

To my son: You are the apex of my heart, the beginning of my joy; a lesson and a teacher. I am grateful for your love and forgiveness. Your strength is the river in which I stride. I will always love you.

To my daughters: In you, I was rebirthed. Your lives gave me a chance of childhood playfulness and pleasure that had escaped my own youthful self. The little girl in me smiled every time each one of you smiled and your laughter shook me to my core. I love you both for your mountainous wisdom and your unfailing support. You are awesome women and I am in awe of all your majesty.

***

Eva slowly stood up and hugged Rachelle, squeezing her tightly and wiping her tears with the palms of her hand. Peaches walked over and handed Rachelle a Kleenex as she wiped the tears from her own face. "I'm so sorry you had to endure all of that pain, especially as a young child." Eva said. "A lot went on in your life. Feeling abandoned by your mother, the sexual abuse, and the shame you felt for making the decision to not tell your boyfriend at the time about him not being the father of your child. These all stem from the same place. You, not feeling safe enough to speak up. I thank you for giving voice to your pain. You've found a therapist that you trust and these are parts of many important steps to healing. Forgiveness is another important step to healing and maintaining your sanity.

Here's what I'd like for you to do; all of you. When you go home, think about who you have not forgiven and write a letter of forgiveness to each person that has offended you. You're not saying, 'I'm okay with what you've done.' What you're saying is, 'I love me more than I hate the pain I've endured.' Next, write a love letter to yourself."

We were all wiping our eyes and taking turns hugging Rachelle. Saying sorry to her sounded like so little to offer after having heard her story.

Rashae's Story
Transformation

The road to Sligoville goes up a winding hill. It passes through luscious green mountains; rugged, soft, and still. At the top of the mountain is a landing. We called it "the square". This is where the old noisy taxi stopped just in front of the butcher's shop, because it could go no further. My aunt briskly slid out, while balancing me in one arm and her uncurling lap. She walked with me and her cousin up the rough grass patch to the middle of a mount. We passed the Baptist Church, with its cobbled stone whitewash walls beseeching villagers to come and worship.

There, my grandmother and her grandchildren worshiped; my grandfather and my aunts and uncles never went to church with us. To the right and first turn

73

off were the narrow paths to the village and the route to our home.

"Ohh deh!" Someone yelled out to my Aunt from Ms. Joyce's shop and rum bar.

"Ole dutty rum head man." She said under her breath, but politely waved back.

We walked passed the "Church of God" another church in our community. As we passed Ms. Brown's pink grocery shop, weeds and knee-high grass from the middle of the road wisped at my aunt's feet. She gleefully skipped around them onto the already trodden stoned track, still carrying me.

At the edge of a dismount that leads to the beginning of the village is a place where I grew to hate. The place with the vinery black gate where 'duppy black heart man' lived. I remember being passed to him. He held me up on his left arm. My dress gave him a shield. The wind kissed my eyes and his hand glided up and squeezed my thighs. Then, I felt his finger pierced into my private parts. I remember the discomfort. I remember my cry. My aunt, surprised by my sudden and what seemed to be an unprovoked scream, quickly grabbed me. This was my first memory as a child.

That moment held me captive for many years and gave me many sleepless nights. When I grew up and felt strong enough to speak up, I told my aunt. She was stunned. "Oh my God! That guy never even held you for a minute. My hand got heavy from carrying you. You started to cry almost immediately and I took you out of his arms." She said. "I can't believe you even remember that day. You were a baby, maybe two years old. I took you to the fair in Spanish Town. You were wearing your yellow ruffled dress."

Yes, I remembered that day. I also remember how my body felt heavy whenever I saw that man again. He was a family member and I saw him quite a few times in our home, parading around in his tight shirt and his wide legged pants as if he had come to town for the in-season fresh fruits. I saw him again at his mother's house when I was thirteen. He was all grown up; well into his thirties. Yet, his wife was a teenager. They sat together on a couch with a baby in her lap. All I could think was. "That poor baby. May God deliver him." I never visited that house again.

When I was three years old I played hopscotch with my mother. My smile was as big as the crescent moon. We were at my grandmother's house which was lined with green bushy willow trees and different shades of orange hibiscus flowers. My mother picked a hibiscus and placed it in my hair. I jumped in the square boxes and the flower fell. She shouted lovingly, "Use it and mark your spot toozle."

One day I stood between her legs as she sat on the foot of the bed and combed my hair. The next day she disappeared. When I asked for her, I was told, "Yu madda gawn a farin, she soon come back". So, I waited. I stayed with my head pressed up against the window pane where I looked down on the front of the yard and watched the gate waiting for my mother to return.

One day while I was waiting, I fell asleep. My head bucked the glass and it broke right into my head. Bright red blood spewed down onto my face and into my ear. "Jesus Christ likkle girl!" Aunty P muffled. She cleaned me up and put a bandage around my head, cuddled me all day instead of baby Rain. I never saw my mother again.

In June of 1976, just six months after my mother disappeared, my father died in a tragic car accident. I still recall the short time I spent with my father. One early morning his big hands held mine as we walked together up the rocky country road to "ground" to get fresh fruits and vegetables. On this particular day we got ginger and green grass that was taller than me, with firm seedy buds. He hung the grass to dry in darkness, then we sat on the stoop of his house. Here he meticulously rolled a tight spliff; licked it across the edge of the paper and sealed it just like you would an envelope. I sat on his lap eating Otaheite apples, he brought the clouds from the sky right in front of my face where I touched God and went to sleep.

At my father's "nine night", I danced with the Kumina dancers around the bar-b-que and skipped alongside the bun, soda, and the white rum. My uncle made them sway to the rhythm of the drummers, beating and chanting sweet melodious words. The audience was clapping and singing, men and women were gyrating to the sound of strong drum beats.

"Falla me…"
"Something, something"
"Falla me…"
"Dung to Riverside, Falla me"
I had no idea that my father was gone and I would forever be without a dad.

When I was five years old, I moved from Sligoville, St. Catherine where I was living with my mother's parents, (mama and dada) as they were affectionately called by us grandchildren. The house was full. There were my four siblings and all "nineteen" of my cousins and counting, and me. I went to live with my great-grandmother in Kingston on Richmond Park road. I was the only child in this house. The quietness was beautiful and I amused myself by exploring the heights of every mango tree in the yard. I combed my great-grandmother's hair and passed time by making several attempts to cut off a mole that grew on the right side of her round and wrinkled chin with a knotted thread. Whatever I wanted to do, we did.

At nights my mind filled with wonder as great grandmother's stories filled my heart. She told me about brother Anansi, brother Tucuma, and the story of the two sisters and the little humped back old lady with the magical rice. In the mornings, my favorite porridge greeted me. It was steaming hot with a slice of bread and butter, or whatever was my breakfast desire. My happiness was my great-grandmother's only concern. The men in this new home were different from the men in Sligoville; at least different from those who touched me and molested me. These men had beautiful girlfriends with very stylish, bright and energetic clothes. When my great-grandmother grew older, the family didn't think she could care for me anymore, so I was moved… again.

I moved to my uncle Papa Nell and his common law wife Ms. Rita's home. They had five children. When I move here, I started first grade. At this home, my cousin

Bonnie was in high school and she made me and my cousins stay outside until it was dark. We played ring games and danced to Rod Stewart's new song, "If you want my body". Papa Nell made us a swing in the backyard and I would swing so hard I could touch the blue in the sky, or even the clouds if I wanted to. We picked sweet cherries from the corner on the side of the house and Miss Rita made cherry juice so delicious that it made your taste buds spring water and rave. I don't remember why I had to leave this house, but I spent all of the first grade there and then when it was time to start second grade I was moved again.

To my surprise, my eldest sister Rachelle was living at my next home with Aunty Elizabeth and her family. My aunt reigned like a queen in this house. Rachelle and I shared a bed and swapped made up stories at night. I told her about the two little girls and the old lady with the magical rice and she told me hilarious stories you would never have imagined. In her stories, pennies and shoes weren't ordinary things. They could talk and carry on with antics because they had a mind of their own. The house began to buzz about Rachelle traveling to America, and soon she was gone.

I lived with Aunty Elizabeth and her family: her husband, three other children, and Miss Jackson (her mother-in-law) until I was in the middle of fifth grade. At Aunty Elizabeth's home, you came straight home from school, did your homework right away, and then went outside to play. "Yu better come inside before it get dark." She would warn. Always waiting with hands on her "kimbo" head tilted down towards her shoulder and eyes wide open with a voice bigger than the Great Grape Ape.

"Likkle red gyal go bade, and don't leave yu panty inna di baachoom or else."

"Yes, Aunty Lizzy."

The family dynamics changed in this home, and I was abruptly sent to live with another aunt, where I ended the fifth grade.

Aunty Dawn's home was in Spanish Town St. Catherine in Del-a-Vega City. She was expecting a new baby and she glided around with a bright face and a hurried look. She sat at her sewing machine making new baby chemises. She smiled often, except when she scolded me; which was usually about me not staying in the house. Her husband loved to celebrate the end of the week, but when he did it frightened me. Though he never touched me inappropriately, I just couldn't trust that he wouldn't. I had been through enough men touching me. So whenever he came home from drinking, if my aunt wasn't home I would go to the neighbor's house or make a big alarm. That didn't work out too well for me and I was sent back to Sligoville.

In spite of all this moving around, I still attended the same primary school off Molynes Road. Traveling to Kingston from Sligoville required waking up earlier. I had to catch a taxi at 6 a.m., a bus by 7 a.m., and another by 7:30 a.m. to be at Tarrant Primary School by exactly 8:00 a.m. By the time I got back to Sligoville in the evening, it was nervously dark and my grandmother said, "Only the ungodly and duppy black heart men walk the road so late." I was only eleven years old and traveling on my own at those hours by myself, made my grandmother anxious. So, I was sent back to

Aunty Lizzy's home with the warning from my grandmother to be good, to listen, and to help her more with chores around the house. I finished sixth grade and did not pass my exam to go to a high school. What a catastrophe!

Options for a stable home and a good secondary education seemed like it was never meant for a girl like me. I began to worry. I was hungry to learn. I wanted to be bright and go to a "big" school, like Ardenne, Queens, St. Hugh's or Immaculate High. Unfortunately, not passing the common entrance exam gave me little options for that luxury and little hope for myself. I would have to settle for any secondary school that had enough space for another student. Even that seemed impossible. In every school I tried to enroll, my aunt was told it was "too full" for another student. I should have passed my exam, I thought. But how could I? My daydreams of my mother kept my mind busy on most days, and on exam day they quieted my mind and lulled me into another planet on the day of my test.

Eventually, Aunty Elizabeth convinced John Mills All age, (an overcrowded school) that if they registered me, she would donate a bench that could hold three students. That worked! I was placed on the evening shift and was to start on Monday. I always loved reading so I continued to read. This time, I read more than the books I had at home. I read the pamphlets and the books from the Jehovah Witnesses, and I read more of the Bible. I read every book at home and then I joined the "Tom Redcam Library" in Cross Roads. Reading took me far and to distant places and showed me who I could be. I loved the library and I stopped going to church on Saturdays and went to the library instead. I felt so free

SE-LAH; WHEN MOMMY LEFT FOR FARIN

and responsible during this time and I looked forward to Saturdays.

The books I was reading had taken me to different worlds and the girls my age in those worlds were unbelievable. They were strong and brave and I wanted to be just like them. In my new world, I was creating a girl who everyone would know was bright; a girl who was brave. I could be a girl like Nancy Drew who solved mysteries, or I could be talented like the beautiful singer Nadine Sutherland. Perhaps I'd be like Mr. Aer, Sligoville's published writer.

One morning while I was on my way to school, I saw Mr. Aer hurrying to the square where we would catch the taxis. It was there he told me, "You must read the newspaper Rashae. Important people do." Then he showed me an article that he wrote in the newspaper. I knew then just what I'd do. I'd write interesting things for important people and publish it in the Gleaner. Maybe that was my calling.

One weekend I left Kingston to visit Sligoville to spend time with my grandparents. My intentions were to head back on Sunday evening, but I missed my taxi. When Sunday came and it was time to go home, I was busy playing with my cousins and taking care of our grandmother. The dark clouds hovered just below the sky that evening with heavy intentions to rain chaos. Someone knocked on the door, and I opened it to see that it was my brother Ricky.

"Yes now, Aunty Lizzy come fi yu." He said with much concern. Aunty Elizabeth made everyone nervous. You never knew when she would bop you to straighten out some imperfection. I was surely going to get it. I thought so, but I remained calm and cool.

"A true, she know seh mi have school tomorrow man. She come fi give me a ride home." I said trying to pretend I wasn't the least bit troubled.

"Aunty Elizabeth?" Surprisingly her arms were not at her kimbo. "Are you okay?" I asked.

"No," she answered. "Mommy died this morning." Her head wasn't tilted to her shoulders. No, her eyes were not wide open and she didn't look upset. In fact, her arms were dropped by the side of her long blue dress and her face looked concerned.

"Miss Jackson is dead?" I asked.

"No, your mommy is dead. She died in a car accident this morning."

"What!?" I asked.

I cried and let out a screeching scream. Everyone on the veranda grew still. Immediately, every ounce of blood that was in me rushed to my head and it swelled so big I felt like it would explode. The news felt so heavy I could hardly stand at that moment. I walked away, but I couldn't hold my weight and my legs gave way. I passed out. I woke up to the smell of ammonia and my grandmother holding me and rocking me. I was in total disbelief.

I can't believe this is happening.

No matter what was going on in my life I was comforted by the pillars of hope that one day soon I would be with my mother; in her world hearing her teaching, her scolding, and her commands. I longed to be comforted by her loving arms and her warm kisses. I wanted to hear her tender voice saying, "There, there, Toozle. I'm here for you and I'll always be here."

Aunty Lizzy reached down and lifted my heavy body up to hers and whispered, "I know it hurts, but pull yourself together. You gotta be stronger now than you've ever been. Look at your brothers and your little sister. They need you."

I picked up my head and glanced around. I could barely see out of my swollen eyes, but I saw the look of hopelessness and despair in the way my brothers and sister sat. Ricky was curled up on the night table and comforting himself. Ron sat outside on the edge of the water tank. I could see him through the window, with his head hanging down and tears rolled from his big eyes as he jabbed a stick in the dirt repeatedly. Rain, not a baby anymore, lay on top of the sheets on the bed in a fetal position. "We have to go and prepare for the embassy. You all need to get a visa so you can go to America for her funeral."

Although the pain I felt ran deeper than the deepest water well, I could hear hope in that sentence. I tried to gather myself as I left Sligoville hurt, angry, and with a heavy heart. Ron had a problem with his birth certificate and he was left behind; abandoned by his closest allies.

We came to the United States to say a formal goodbye to the mother we yearned for, but never had.

My siblings and I decided that even though she was not in our day to day lives, she must have loved us. Why else would she have bothered to send all those pretty clothes and birthday cards with the crisp five dollar bill? So we were going to honor her with a poem.

Lovely dainty Spanish needle,
With your yellow flower and white,
Dew bedecked and softly sleeping,
Do you think of me to-night?

Shadowed by the spreading mango,
Nodding o'er the rippling stream,
Tell me, dear plant of my childhood,
Do you of the exile dream?

Do you see me by the brook's side
Catching crayfish 'neath the stone,
As you did the day you whispered:
Leave the harmless dears alone?
Do you see me in the meadow
Coming from the woodland spring
With a bamboo on my shoulder
And a pail slung from a string?

Do you see me all expectant
Lying in an orange grove,
While the swee-swees sing above me,
Waiting for my elf-eyed love?

Lovely dainty Spanish needle,
Source to me of sweet delight,
In your far-off sunny southland
Do you dream of me to-night?

–By: Claude McKay–

In America, we waited for the day to come to say our farewell to our mom. We were told by our Aunt Rose who lived downstairs from my mother's attic apartment (we were now living with her) that our mother had to be buried soon after her death, because the funeral home was charging too much money to keep her, and the embassy took too long to give us the Visa. She told us not to worry, as soon as she found some time off from visiting Katherine (who was in the car with mom, and was now hospitalized from her injuries) she would take us to the gravesite. We never saw our mother.

I had more siblings. My big sister Rachelle was there, along with my little brothers Raven and Ryan, and my little sisters Rory and baby Ruby. I got busy asking them about themselves, and what they liked. They showed me around their home and took me up the winding stairs to the attic where their bedrooms were. The next day they took us to their favorite park.

I spent the summer of 1986 playing games; double dutch, water balloon, dodgeball, and racing in the streets. That summer, I also learned how to ride a bicycle. Soon, it was time to get ready for school. I learned that high school was a right, not a privilege, for every teenager in America as long as they wanted it. They didn't have to pass any national exam. As long as you passed your class you went straight to high school. Yes! I hungered for it.

I started school and made some friends. We went skating at Skate Key on Friday nights and to the

Whitestone Cinema on Saturday evenings. All the boys were watching us girls, but there was one who was very persistent with me. He really liked me and eventually, my feelings grew for him. He became my boyfriend. He called me often and wanted to "take me out".

"Out where?! Yu mussy mad! Tell him, me seh if him want, him can come here and di two a yu sit down in di living room and talk, like teenagers, but yu naw go nuh weh wid no baddy." My Aunt Rose uttered with a seething tone.

We made plans for him to come to my home. In the living room was a thick brown and gold couch set, covered neatly with thick plastic. I sat at the end of one chair and he sat across from me on the love seat. He stretched his hand across the round glass top center table with gold leaf edges and reached out for mine. I dare not reach back and offer him my hand. Just behind him and past the dining room, my Aunt Rose was in the kitchen sipping tea from a large cup that read, "Mum has a green thumb". When I didn't see her I giggled harder at his jokes and he sang, "I think we're alone now", with his own twist.

"I think you're alone now... Don't seem to see Miss Green thuuuumb around."

We laughed out loud and made plans for the next date. After a year, he began to pressure me for sex. One night we went to a house party that was up the street from my house. I had a Heineken or two and then we went for a ride. A few weeks later, I noticed that my body was tired all the time and I couldn't stay awake during the days after school. I would find a quiet space anywhere in the house to sleep. The house was big, but there was no place to hide. One day, in the middle of washing the dishes, my eyes were so heavy with sleep I decided to lie down. I hid underneath my aunt's bed. I just knew no one would look there. One of my adult cousins found me.

"I've been watching you lately," she started, "you can hardly keep your eyes open, now I find you sleeping underneath the bed. Are you pregnant?"

"Pregnant? No, I'm just very tired lately." I answered.

"Are you having sex?" she asked. I didn't know what to say.

"Yes." I answered.

"Well, tomorrow I'm taking you to Planned Parenthood. If you're not pregnant, you have to start taking some vitamins, and you definitely have to start on some kind of birth control."

***

The walk to Planned Parenthood was long, but the wait for the results was even longer. So many thoughts raced through my head while I sat patiently in the waiting area. The books and magazines piled up on the table beside me suggested that I could get all the help I needed from the doctors here. I was fifteen years old. I had no parents and eight siblings. My grandmother warned me to make the best of my opportunity, but here I was in a women's health clinic waiting to hear if I was pregnant. The nurse practitioner walked out and called me.

I was pregnant.

The weirdest thing happened at that moment. My heart that had been so heavy with worry, became light and joyful. The thought that I was going to have a baby made me happy and hopeful.

When I told my Aunt Rose that I was pregnant, her reaction was not the same. She was shocked and she scrambled to figure out how to handle the news. She sent me away to live with one of her sisters in Brooklyn, NY. While I was there, my aunt and I discussed me going to school and continuing my education. She told me I needed some new clothes and an appointment with a gynecologist.

One day, we went shopping first and then to the gynecologist appointment. The gynecologist explained an abortion procedure to me in detail. I said, "Sir, you must have the wrong person because I am not here to have an abortion." He asked me my name again and said, "Yes, I am very sorry young lady. I was told that you wanted an abortion, but I am not doing this. I will not do this without your consent." His pink face turned beet red and he dashed out.

That evening, all my aunts came together for a meeting. At the meeting, they were set on the porch like a choir of judges and I was at the bottom of the steps with my two brown shopping bags. The choir of judges made it very clear.

"You are going to have an abortion or leave this house."

"You are a bad influence for your sisters!"

"So disappointed in you."

"Ungrateful."

"Weh di hell yu going to put pickney? A must pon yu head."

"How are you going to feed a child, yu nuh si seh a nine a unu yu madda dead left?"

I felt the attacks coming from all angles and I couldn't take it anymore, so I picked up my brown paper bags and said, "Thank you all for everything you have done. I'm leaving now." As I walked away, I heard my cousin Katherine say, "I don't know where you are going, but I will always be here for you. I love you cuz."

I walked off with my bags in hand and tears streaming down my face. I walked to the pay phone and called my boyfriend. He and his family took me in. There, his sister Kelly and I were the same age, and their father said we were to share her room. She was happy to have me and she gave me the side of the room with the bookcase.

We talked about what was happening in her life and the plans she had for her future. We stayed up late nights giggling and laughing ourselves silly. She told me she had a boyfriend and I told her to go to Planned Parenthood for birth control, or she would end up pregnant. Soon after, my boyfriend and I got our own basement apartment. It became our home.

At sixteen years old, I became a mom. It was the most beautiful gift; a divine blessing and a deliverer in one baby boy. I bathed him early in the morning and brushed his curly hair. I sang to him and rocked him in my bosom. He was my joy. No one told me that he would cry all the time. It was so hard to take care of myself, the baby, and the apartment. There was just so much to do. I was exhausted and my boyfriend worked all day.

Life got hard and I struggled to keep it together. To my surprise, my boyfriend had a temper, but I had the heart of a lion. He was imperfectly good, strong, and giving; he said he loved me. He gave me the first place I called "my home", with my own bed, my own sofa, and my very own chest of drawers. There was no more moving to the next home. This was my home and I loved him for his goodness.

I went back to school one month after our baby was born. It was a school where young mothers like myself could take our babies to class with us. Then, I transitioned to the standard high school where things were much more difficult. I found a well-recommended babysitter who told me about public assistance. I went to the welfare office and they told me they could only give me food stamps, because I was undocumented. I learned to shop using coupons. I would buy a week's worth of groceries with $60.00 and a pocket full of coupons.

I started a routine and did what I had to do. I expended enough effort to get my high school diploma a year earlier than scheduled. Cosmetology school was my next mission. Before I knew it, I was a licensed beautician with more children; a perfect family. However the heated rage within our home became an ongoing problem.

My boyfriend was either constantly accusing me of cheating or he was jealous of everyone and everything. He screamed and I screamed. He would hit me and I would cut right back into him. It was volatile, and in those moments our children had no voice. I saw myself in their muteness and wondered how could I do that to them? Would they get a chance at happiness or would sadness steal their hearts? My worst nightmare was if I would disappear and leave them for the world to use and abuse them? Would they be the next generation destined for abandonment? I wanted to give them more, but I didn't know how. I wanted to be there to protect them and guide them, and I didn't want to break up our home. Yet, I wasn't sure I had the strength to endure the violence in the house, and I didn't want to. This guy was taking more than he gave. Coming home became a necessary burden. I lost my smile.

Beautifying others empowered me. My clients talked and I listened. They valued me. But, I still had not become the powerful girl I dreamt I would be. What I became was two-faced. During the day at the salon, I was independent and inspiring. At home, I moped around with unkempt hair, dragging myself through the house in a green bathrobe and no smile. One day my son who was now about ten years old asked me, "Mom why are you always mad? Are you upset with me?" I looked up at my reflection in the glass cupboard door. The girl looking back was not me. I didn't know who she was. I had died somewhere along the way and a sad motherfucker had taken my place.

In my attempt to hold a grudge for all the pain I had been through, my heart became occluded. Sadness consumed me and I needed no reason to cry. I saw no way out. There was no hope and I wanted to explode. I just wanted to end it all. I started to think of ways to end my life and waited for the perfect opportunity. I started imagining driving off of a bridge, or falling asleep and not ever waking up. Instead, I prayed and started to read the bible again. I knew the Word and I knew God's promises for me.

Psalms 46 said: *"God is our refuge and strength, an ever-present help in trouble. Therefore we will not fear, though the earth give way and the mountains fall into the heart of the sea, though its waters roar and foam and the mountains quake with their surging. Selah"*

The depression did not go away just yet. I woke up the next day determined to unload any extra burden, and I cut off all my hair. I became physically ill from my pain, worry, and feelings of defeat, so I called my pastor. He immediately prayed for me. He told me I needed to forgive and make a plan for my future, so I did. I planned for an independent life without the burden and the agony of my relationship, and without the pain of my memories growing up. I got on my knees and prayed for joy and peace, and to be present for my children.

I'd been wanting to become a nurse since elementary school. I was a member of the Red Cross and it was my passion. When I was fourteen, I saved a guy's life who had a stab wound, and the emergency room doctor told me I should become a nurse or a doctor. I decided to go back to school and become a nurse. My now husband and many others thought I was ridiculous. "Who would leave dem own business and go work fi people?" He asked.

It made sense, but I was determined. My journey began. "I'm going to become a nurse." Our children beamed with pride when I shared the news. I started school, and they were encouraging.

I ran the beauty salon in the days, did homework with the children in the evening, and went to school at nights. Nursing school introduced me to organizations that empowered me and made me reflect on my value. I learned to forgive myself for the things I'd done and I learned to forgive others for the things they'd done to me. My husband and I went to marriage counseling and began getting the tools we needed to be better partners and better parents. We practiced better communication skills and our relationship improved.

To my family: Your existence gave me purpose, but your support gave me hope.

To my children: As I watch you write your own story on your blank canvases, I am in awe of your superior strength and the greatness you possess. I thank God for his mercies and pray for his continued favor in your lives. For my grandchildren, here and yet to be, be phenomenal. You are phenomenally made.

When I finished telling my story Eva gave me a big hug and told me how much she admired my strength and how I handled my challenges. She encouraged me and all the ladies to keep a grateful journal.

SE-LAH; WHEN MOMMY LEFT FOR FARIN

Kelly's Story
Restoration

I met Rashae when I was in high school. I was in the tenth grade. We had a mutual friend who had a sleepover party. At the party, we got dressed up and we did each other's hair. She did mine and burned me on my ear. My hair looked so pretty though, that the burn felt like a reward. She is still my favorite hairdresser thirty-five years later, and she doesn't even do damn hair anymore!

One day I found out she was dating one of my older brothers and before I knew it, just like that we were sharing my room. She was like a sister to me and a mother to my younger brother. My brothers and I had just lost our mother to cancer, not even a year before. The loss was hard. Rashae joining our family felt refreshing.

As soon as she came, I believed her strength was impressive. At first, I felt she was a little too bossy to my five-year-old brother and too much of a disciplinarian. I remember one day when he was doing something she thought was wrong for "a boy of his age", she called him over like she was a grown woman. She put her hands at her "kimbo", tilted her head to her shoulder, leaned into him, opened her eyes big and wide and scolded him. I thought to myself, "who the hell does she think she is?" That was my baby brother and he could do whatever he had been doing around here! Soon it became evident that she loved the baby and he was going to be okay with her.

Of my parents ten children, I am the only girl. So when Rashae moved in, she was a pleasure that took some time getting used to. My father warned me that from now on she and I would be sharing a room. She came in and read all my books, told me about them, and told me all kinds of other stories. I loved how she told stories, especially the ones from the Bible. The stories sounded so different. The characters were so real; they live with me even now. We talked and laughed and a sisterhood developed.

After I lost my mother, I had become more concerned about my five year old baby brother. I took him everywhere with me; supermarket, farmers market, butchers shop, you name it. Whatever I was buying I asked him his opinion, from toothpaste to maxi pads. When he didn't understand what I was buying, he gave me a puzzled look and shrugged his shoulders. He carried the shopping bags, helped me cook, and assisted me in doing chores.

When Rashae moved in, she noticed I was doing way too much. She divided the chores among everyone in the house. Instead of me cooking every day, I only cooked on Sundays and one other day in the week. My dad cooked on his days off from work. Rashae cooked once a week, and all my brothers cooked at least one day each week. Soon I had more time to do my homework and other things; like dating.

I had a boyfriend and excitedly told Rashae, since we were being sisters and all. I couldn't believe her reaction. She actually sat me down and gave me "the talk". "If you are going to have sex you betta be careful. Go to Planned Parenthood," she instructed. "Make sure you get birth control pills so you don't get pregnant, and condoms so you don't get any STDs. Don't ever have sex without a condom unless your intention is to get pregnant." She hurled, as she pointed her finger. I was being schooled by a pregnant fifteen-year-old.

High school was remarkable. I excelled and finished well above average. The months leading up to my graduation were filled with award ceremonies almost weekly. I wasted no time, and went straight to college after graduation. I worked full-time and went to school full-time. I couldn't wait to become a social worker. Being motherless and having to take care of my brother and help out in the family was hard, but I graduated college magna cum laude.

Excited to start my life, I began my career at a hospital in the Bronx, and then moved on to an even more challenging position at the Legal Aid Society of New York. The children there put life in real perspective and gratitude filled my heart. I was thankful that although I didn't have a mother, when she died I wasn't a vulnerable child like the ones I worked for. I still had my dad and my brothers. While working at the Legal Aid Society, the pain of my mother's death emerged more often. I silenced it by giving more of myself to the children I served.

Some of my friends were getting married and I was sure I wanted the same thing for me. One Memorial Day weekend, my friends and I went on our annual getaway to Virginia Beach. There I met a handsome guy. He was tall and lean with beautiful pale gold eyes. Our dates were adventurous and crossed a few state lines. Our love was infectious and full of wild dreams. We did anything for each other. Not too long after we started dating, he asked me to marry him and of course I said yes! Our families came from all over to celebrate our bliss.

He had already had a baby girl and I welcomed them both into my life with open arms. My father, the first man I loved, walked me down the aisle and gave me away. I thought he looked tired, but he insisted he was just overwhelmed with happiness. I was sure I noticed he had a sad sway, but he said he was glad he was alive and able to give his only daughter away, to be someone's wife. My husband and I ended the auspicious occasion with a beautiful kiss.

About a year later we received joyous news. We were expecting a baby! It felt like a double holiday with back to back four day weekends. I moved to Virginia permanently and began to make plans to welcome a new member to our family. I was almost certain that my father was ill, so I gave him my all. I called him daily and he gave me advice about how to take care of a new baby. One day he told me that he couldn't pee so he was going to the doctor. My father was later diagnosed with prostate cancer.

When that journey began, it was like I already knew. I could see pain in my father's eyes and I heard it through his laughter when we spoke over the phone. He remained the strong and resilient man I always knew and insisted on cooking for his family every weekend.

Our baby boy was born bouncing and strong and ready to warm our hearts. My father met our baby and blessed him with his love. We spent his last days talking and laughing through his pain. During that time of weakness and vulnerability, my father gave me some good counsel and I will cherish his advice forever. One musky November morning in the year 2006, while watching CNN as President Bush made an announcement about Saddam Hussein, I got a phone call that my father had passed.

***

The day I found out that I was having a second child couldn't have been more special. I ran from the car into the house and up the stairs. Boiling over with excitement I jumped up in the air and into my husband's arms. "We're having another baby!" I screamed.

We began to make plans to welcome another baby. We were a growing family and needed a bigger home. Both our hearts were blessed when we welcomed our baby girl into our world.

In the year 2010, on March 5th. I found out that I was expecting my third child. Even though I already had two children the news of a third brought me an insurmountable feeling of pure elation. My previous plans to go to New York to see my niece's performance in her high school play "Evilene", could not have come sooner. I couldn't wait to tell everyone that I would be having another baby due October 13, 2010. Why should I wait until I passed my first trimester? Nothing was going to happen. I had two wonderful, healthy children. There was no doubt that this one would be the same.

When I got to New York, I beamed with delight and glowed with pleasure. I could feel every cell in my body illuminate as my baby grew. Rashae knew the minute she looked at me. I barely got out the car before we started jumping for joy, dancing like two silly girls. I really didn't have to tell anyone. Just by looking at me, they could tell I was carrying a child.

"How yu just a glow so?"

"Whe yu mean, how mi look?"

"Like yu pregnant."

"A tru?"

"Nobody else no tell yu so?"

"Yes man, mi pregnant fi tru."

"Treee pickney now?"

"Mi know seh yu have one bwoy pickney and a likkle girl."

"Yes mi dear."

"God bless yu, yu look good bad."

"Tanks mi dear."

Everyone was happy for me. I never felt so confident in a pregnancy before. At my next visit with the gynecologist, I was told that my baby was just the size of a "rice grain", but oh how I nursed that belly, just like I did before with the other two.

One night my body had a feeling of intense uncertainty. Earlier that day I had been in a heated screaming match with my husband over a relationship he had with someone that I thought was an enigma. As I laid in my bed waiting to fall asleep, I began to review the conversations and emotions. The feelings, in review, were much more intense than the words we spewed. During my recollections an emptiness gushed over me and I could hardly wait for the morrow to be.

Sleep escaped me that night and the darkness turned to day as I tossed and turned in my bed. I counted down the hours until it was time to call the doctor. They said to come right away. I had mixed emotions; happy that the morning had finally broke free, yet anxious as I wondered if my baby was okay. As I drove to the doctor's office, I worried about the gush of water that flowed from beneath me last night.

I parked my car, got out, and locked it. I took a final deep breath before walking inside the clinic's doors. The doctor was gentle, but he wanted to be sure, so a sonogram was ordered and indeed there was no heartbeat. Our baby had died within me.

Why would this happen to me? How could this be? I wanted to scream, but my voice wasn't there. Whatever took my baby was dismantling me.

"I'm sorry to say this," the doctor said, "but these things happen quite frequently."

That was no consolation. My baby was dead. How could death reach into me, my protective womb, and steal our child? He explained the process my body would experience. I heard him, but I wished this nightmare would go away, and I walked out of his office in denial. The nightmare did not go away. Instead, I had to go home and wait for the miscarriage. All sorts of thoughts traveled through my head. My conscience was eating me alive.

"How could a thing like this happen to me?"

"What did I do?"

"What did my husband do?"

"Did we do this?"

"Is this our fault?"

"Did we deserve this?"

"Was this a punishment for something either of us had done?"

About a day had passed and I started to feel the cramps that the doctor described as, "the process".

"WHY Lord! WHY ME?" I cried.

I prayed; pleading for the Lord to restore the life of my baby again and tuck it back in my womb secretly. The thought that death was inside of me, frightened me. I was scared, angry, and couldn't stop crying. The slightest noise startled me. For days I couldn't find my voice. I didn't know what to say or how to say it. I blamed myself for arguing and saying mean things. "Maybe mi shoulda neva cus so much Bomboclaat."

I wanted to share both the burden and the blame, so I told my husband every detail of what I was going through. It hit him like a mac truck. I watched as his brown skin turned pale. I told him it was all his fault and I blamed him for arguing with me and getting me so upset. He didn't defend himself at all. Instead he just stayed still. A part of me felt pleased that he was upset. I wanted to win. Another part of me was angry, hurt, and ashamed. I didn't keep my baby safe.

I had to take some time off from work. I never wanted to see my coworkers again. I worried what they would say or think. I would have to say what happened to me and tell them that I am not carrying a baby anymore. I was filled with shame and embarrassment. I didn't want to talk about what happened. The pain I felt was too strong. When the time got closer for me to go to work, I started looking for another job. I couldn't face those people. I couldn't tell them what I'd been through. Thoughts of how I would explain not being pregnant anymore raced through my head, and I couldn't think of a good lie.

When I returned to work, my co-workers questioned my absence. I didn't know what to say, so I just told them I lost my baby. Everyone was so supportive. To my surprise, other women there had similar experiences. One guy said his wife had eight miscarriages before they gave up trying. A nurse practitioner I spoke to said she lost her baby when she was five months pregnant. I asked her if she was upset or arguing with anyone before she lost the baby; she said no.

"What was the reason for me losing my baby, and how could it happen so unexpectedly? How could my body pull such a nasty mean trick on me?" I asked a coworker.

"My dear it happens to more women than you think and there are no clear answers why." My coworker responded. She seemed to be in a good place, though I knew that would never be me. Hearing that I didn't do anything to cause me losing my baby comforted me for a while and I started to feel a little better.

I thought about my co-worker's wife who experienced eight miscarriages. I couldn't imagine feeling that pain over and over again. If my one miscarriage left my husband and me in such despair, how did others, especially mothers, deal with it multiple times? The thought of my baby, and the prematurely taken life, never goes away. Every October, I remember the expected birth date and sometimes it brings tears to my eyes. I ask myself, would it have been a girl or a boy or twins?

In the beginning, the pain was throbbing and unbearable. It's still there, but dulled by the pleasures and pain of raising two children. I read God's word daily and I meditate on the scriptures. Psalm 3:4 is simple, but it gives me hope: *"I cried unto the Lord with my voice and He heard me out of his holy hill. Selah."*

I thank God every day for my children and I will never take them for granted. They are the beautiful reasons my heart still sings.

***

"Your story is touching." Eva began as she walked over to Kelly and hugged her. "So many women go through this pain. If you are not yet in therapy, please don't overlook this very important part of healing. There are support groups out there for you and women like you who have gone through this tough experience. It doesn't matter how long or how recent it is; seek therapy."

DENISE NICHOLSON

True's Story
Deliverance

The heart of Evil is not black. It's red like yours and mine, and it beats 149 times each minute. I know because I saw the heart of Evil pounding outside of his chest, and I counted every rise as he lay dying in his bed. Evil lived with me and my family until he was dead. Before he was sick he was a real prick, but when he got weak justice was served. I don't know if his weakness and dependence was a final punishment for all his wrong doings. All I know is that when Evil reigned in my home, he was dreadful.

I lived in the Bushwick side of Brooklyn, New York where the summertime heat was thick and hazy. My mother was a registered nurse who worked at Kings County Hospital on the graveyard shift. My father worked there during the day as a handyman. Our home was a two-story family house, which sat tightly packed in the middle of the block. When my mother left for work, my brothers and I had to go straight to bed. If not, Evil would stomp his way through our home looking for a problem. When he finally found one, he took out his black leather wrinkled belt, lined us all up together (me and my two brothers), stripped us down naked, and whooped us until he was tired. Then, we were sent to kneel in a corner on the wooden floor. While we knelt naked in the corner he told us his usual story:

"When I was a boy growing up in Jamaica, my father used to send me five miles early in the mornings, to catch water to bring back to the house. If I didn't do that dawg nwam mi suppa." He said while wrapping his hand around the belt, halfway panting. It's like he got some sort of satisfaction from afflicting that pain on us.

Evil was a damn liar. I know he was never a boy. In fact, Evil had no clue what children did or the games they played, or any idea of what childhood was. I thought children of all sorts must be aliens to him because everything we did had to be explained.

"What you doing over there?" His musty voice said.

"This is a slinky, dad."

"I said what is that you're doing?"

"I'm playing with it dad."

"What is it doing?"

"It's not doing anything, just a toy that wiggles like a worm."

"Yu have attitude? Get dat stupid thing out of mi sight." Then a shoe would come flying straight into my side. Only the devil was so dark and cold, and didn't like children or children's friends.

At the age of nine, I asked my mother's permission to go around the corner to a friend's house to play. "Yes darling." She said. "Go and come back before it gets dark outside."

About an hour later the doorbell rang, and my friend's mom called out, "True, your father is at the door!"

I used to call him father a long time ago when he would make us all breakfast and call us to eat. I called him father when he used to kiss me goodbye when I was going off to school. I called him father when he stayed in the kitchen and waited up with me as I did my homework at the kitchen table. Suddenly everything changed, though. My mother would leave for work and I didn't have a chance to sit at the table for ten minutes to do my homework before I would hear, "Go to yu bed now." Which was often followed by a beating or a hard slap.

Although I called him father, I was sure he had turned into the devil, so I cautiously walked to the door when my friend's mother told me he was there. There he stood like the pied piper with all the neighborhood kids behind him. He grabbed me out of the house and beat me all the way back home. The worst part of the beating was when we got to the big tree in front of one of the neighbor's houses, he held me upside down by one leg and beat me for all to see. That was the beginning of the summer vacation for all the kids in the neighborhood, but the last day for me. I never stepped foot back outside that summer. I just couldn't think of a good excuse for why my father beat me.

One morning while taking a bath and getting ready to go to school my dad opened the bathroom door and yelled, "Didn't I tell you that I left a piece of cake for each one of you to eat."

"Yes dad I ate mine." I said, as I stood naked in the tub and trying to cover my private parts.

"So who left the table yesterday and didn't eat their cake?"

"I don't know daddy, I ate mine." I gave him a look of disgust as he tried to have an argument with me while I was naked in the tub.

At that point, he picked up the bathroom scrub brush that is used to clean the tub and rushed at me. He hit me and I fell in the tub and hit my head. All I saw was blinking star lights spinning. I woke up to the biggest and most intense headache ever and hearing my mother's voice yelling. "True are you okay? Why didn't you go to school? Why are you sleeping in the tub?" She asked with a puzzled look on her face.

I told my mother everything. Not long after that incident, in December of that year one of my mother's sisters came from Jamaica to live with our family. Mom said from now on our aunt was going to help take care of us when she went to work. Our new aunt had a soft and tender voice just like my mother. She often hummed, but mostly she was quiet. Somehow, her quietness hushed my father and he barely had anything to say to me and my brothers anymore. If he had anything to say to us he would wait until aunty was gone for the weekend.

He would lash out at us for simple things, but he easily calmed and went about his business. He spent most of his time out of the house and he seemed less irritable when they finally came in. Aunty made sure I bathed in the evenings and combed my big hair. She made the most delicious food. My favorite was her fried dumplings.

One day I was so eager to eat the dumplings that I went to get it straight out of the hot pot on the stove. The pot, the hot oil, and the dumplings fell over onto my foot and I still have that scar to this day. I remember Aunty bathing my foot until it cooled, and scolding me about not waiting. She was firm, but her voice was still kind.

She stayed in our home for a while. Those days were filled with laughing, singing, and playing hopscotch. She bought me my favorite shoes, which were the black shiny patent leather Mary Janes with a crossover strap and matching black daisies on the sides. I wore it all day until it was time for me to go to bed. Then Aunty had a baby and she left our home. No soon after she left, my dad resumed barking at everyone in the house. I did my best to stay out of his way. My room became my world and a sanctuary where I avoided Evil.

When I was home alone I took an interest in baking. I loved the science and magic of it. I especially enjoyed seeing that the magic came from me. Everyone praised me when they tasted the cakes I baked. They told me how pretty the frosting looked, how moist the cake was, and how perfect my cakes always were. Once my confidence grew, I decided to get a job.

At the age of sixteen, I had my first job working in an Ice-cream store on the weekends. One evening after a long day of scooping ice-cream, mopping the floors, and washing silver ice cream scoopers all day long, I returned home tired as a dog. My father was in the kitchen standing in front of the sink filled with dirty dishes.

"Who left these dirty dishes in the sink?" He barked.

"I don't know daddy, I just got home from work."

He slapped me so hard, I heard a ringing sound vibrate through my head. The ringing was a high frequency, strong like that of an urgent siren, and it blocked out all the other sounds around me. Then it lowered into a faint whisper. I touched my ear and my earring was bent. That day I swore, the next time he ever hit me I was gonna drop his ass on that floor. A multitude of angels must have come down and held me back, because I felt my heart racing and my fist clenched, yet I stood resiliently and did as I was told. "Wash up dem tings weh inna di sink, learn fi keep di place clean, yu is a girl." This was the first time the pain was so intense. I felt shame, loathing, and sadness burning in my skin.

On that day, I decided that I would never speak to my father again. My silence was powerful and it gave me strength. I spoke only to whom I wished and whenever I pleased. It injured my father and made him weak. I saw him looking at me and snarling his teeth, wishing I would speak to him; I said nothing.

After months of not speaking to him, one morning he came into my room and said, "For as long as I shall live don't you ever call me daddy or father or any damn thing ever again. As far as I'm concerned, your father is dead."

Although Evil was a damn liar, this statement was true. I knew all along that my father must have been dead and this man living in his skin was Evil instead. Marching around here tall as a tree and dark as night, with his face partially covered with a wooly beard that stretched from his sideburns, under his nose down to his chin. He tried to hide the darkness within, but I was on to him. I was not fooled no matter who he was pretending to be. He was just pure evil reigning heavily in our home.

When I was seventeen, Evil accused me of hiding the remote control from him. It had been more than a year of silence between us and he had started to show signs of wearing down. It was becoming more evident that I was winning this battle. So this was his opportunity to pick a fight he thought he would win. He approached me with shoulders rolled back and his chest high in the air. "Why you hide the remote?" He barked.

I said nothing, but I knew if he hit me today I was going to drop his ass on that floor. He raised his hand to hit me and that was all I needed. I knew it was time to fight back; no more beatings and no more slaps. I was not timid or shy. I was tall and strong, and I would not be shamed.

I firmly blocked his hand and grabbed him in his chest. I tried to drop him, but he was too heavy. Instead, I pushed him up against the refrigerator with all my might. He was so shocked his eyes popped out of his head in disbelief. I was even more shocked, because I didn't know where this superwoman strength came from. What I did know was that I was sick and tired of Evil reigning in my house. I realized quickly that I was in control, so I widened my gait and opened up my eyes and stared right into his. "No more! NO MORE!!! You are not going to hit me or anyone in this house anymore."

My uncle was visiting us that day and he ran to separate us. He then gave my father some counseling that night. "Listen, man. This is a woman now. Learn this now or yu wi end up dead. When you get a woman angry, dem coming back like an arrow, straight fi yu heart. Neva you hit a woman, they will kill yu as soon as dem get di chance." My Uncle warned him.

He never hit any of us again.

There were no subjects for Evil to reign upon in our home anymore. We all were adults now, and each of us had proven to him that we were strong. He was left to spend much of his time by himself. Our home became quiet. I felt no peace however, as a persistent conflict lived within me.

At nights I'd lie in stillness trying to sleep, as visions of the protracted war between me and my dad came flashing back at me. When sleep did visit me it was punctuated by pictures of naked children getting spanked with a wrinkled, black leather belt by a tall, black man. During the days or waking moments, an unwelcome nervousness haunted me. It was hard to confide in anyone about my ruminations and my experiences in my home. Eventually, I mustered the courage to tell my neighbor. She was encouraging. "Girl you have to learn to pray. There are some things you just have to let go and let God take care of it."

She explained the power of prayer and she encouraged me to pray. I believed her and I started to pray. First I said the Lord's Prayer. I knew it well. Then, I found a scripture that spoke directly to me. It helped me deal with all my long years of pent up pain.

Psalms 55:4-7 read:
My heart is in anguish within me;
The terrors of death have fallen on me.
Fear and trembling have beset me;
Horror has overwhelmed me.
I said, "Oh, that I had the wings of a dove!
I would fly away and be at rest.
I would flee far away
and stay in the desert. Selah.

I read it and wept and prayed that I would be healed. I continued taking Advanced Placement classes and did very well in high school. I always made the honor roll and that made me very proud. When it came time to go to college, I could pick, choose, and refuse because I had multiple acceptance letters. Choosing to stay local was the only choice I felt I had. I was too injured and fragile to be living away and among others.

I completed college, interviewed, and began my career. It was an exciting time to begin my independent life. Instead of moving out, I remained at home and basked in my successes. When I was 27 years old, my father called a family discussion. At my father's request, everyone met at the dinner table. I reluctantly went. My two brothers were there standing with broad shoulders, skeptic faces, and invisible scars. My mother sat with her hand to her jaw looking like a worn out Florence Nightingale. Everyone was waiting to hear what would be said.

My father emerged, rolling in a wheelchair; not looking like the warrior I knew, fought, and still have an ongoing cold war with. Now he looked more like a wounded soldier. As he wheeled himself into the room, my heart sank and I didn't want to remember our years of conflict and that we were still at war. To my surprise and to everyone in the room, he acknowledged all of his mistakes and erred ways. He confessed he had not always been a good parent or a good husband, but that he was only doing what he thought was best. He then bowed his head in shame and asked us for forgiveness.

It was hard to hear him. He sounded so meek; the first time in a long time I heard tenderness in his voice. His tempered tone in seeking forgiveness for himself was like a traumatic infliction on me. He said he was newly baptized and a born-again Christian. *How convenient,* I thought.

My father was fighting a losing battle with Diabetes Mellitus and now he wanted to make things right before he died. His condition required having both legs and five fingers amputated and he was now confined to a wheelchair. I didn't want to forgive him. I wanted to find scriptures that said if you were evil and did unkind things you don't deserve to be forgiven and you're going to hell; but I never found that. The more I read the Bible, the more I found that God is loving, kind, merciful, and he loves us all. No matter who we are or what we've done, once we repent, he will forgive us.

Matthew 6:14-15: *"For if you forgive other people when they sin against you, your heavenly Father will also forgive you. But if you do not forgive others for their sins, your Father will not forgive your sins"*

When I was twenty-nine, my father passed away on my younger brother's birthday. That was the last wound he inflicted. I don't know if his strong and independent body was eventually mutilated as a final punishment for all his wrongdoings. All I know is I took care of him when he needed me. My neighbor told me that all things work well for those who love the Lord. Maybe my being there and taking care of him in his final days was a divine blessing from God who knows all our hearts and our intentions. Who knows if my father was just doing the best he knew how? All I know is this, I was kind to him until his very last breath. I am grateful to God that he taught me to forgive. Forgiveness gave me wings like a dove and my heart is free."

***

Eva walked over to True and flung her arms wide open, giving her a big hug. They stood in the middle of the room hugging each other and rocking. "True you are a real child of God to love even your enemies." She said. "You were at war with your father, but when he got weak and vulnerable, you put your feelings aside and loved him and cared for him. God bless you."

"I love you all." She said. "You have been through some hardships. Yet, you are all here with life and hope for your lives."

Tasha's Story
The Chief Cornerstone

"Yu si you, yu is a dam blasted liad!"

"Mi ago tek mi tings dem and come outta dis yawd."

"Mi doh waa si yu eena mi sight."

"Come outta mi face bwoy an gwane a yu gyal yawd."

"A have a good feelin fi bun up yu tings dem."

"Watch mi."

"Dam blasted whoring man."

"Me a go tek my pickney dem an go bout mi business."

"Bought yu have baby madda a road."

"Outta auda."

I watched my mother stand outside in the yard holding the hem of her tube top yellow cotton dress balled up in her hands and tucked between the top of her knees. She was standing a few feet in front of my father, but she paced back and forth towards him. She walked up to him spewing her venomous words. Each time she ended a sentence she walked away. She made a few steps back in front of him and then she would wheel her skirt tail, turn around in front of him, and start the ritual all over again.

After the quarrel, my parents separated and I was told there was a court hearing and a decision by the judge for me to go and live with my father. My sister was to stay in the custody of my mother, because my mother accused our father of not treating her the same way he treated me.

When I went to live with my father and his new girlfriend, no one spoke to me but him. In his absence I was not spoken to at all. The woman was busy taking care of her baby and caring for her home. I was in her way. She complained to my father and I was quickly taken away.

I held my dad's hand and he tucked me into his bright orange Mini Cooper. We headed for a ride to my grandmother's home. We stopped only to buy a warm duck bread as a treat for my grandma and grandpa. The day I arrived at my grandmother's house, there was a tall dark complexioned woman in the yard hanging clothes on the line. She looked over her shoulder when she heard my father's car. The smile on her face when she looked at me made my body warm, and I fell in her arms when she knelt down to hug me.

I loved living with my grandmother and my papa. Even though I was the only child living in the house, I was happy. Whatever I asked for they went out of their way to give me. I awoke in the morning to a fresh breeze that made the tamarinds, bananas, and coconut trees wave their leaves in unison, always gently at me. The pimento trees stood firm and their narrow shiny leaves quivered. I spent much of my afternoons playing in the river and climbing any number of fruit trees. At the top of the mango, papaya, and guava trees, was my favorite place to be. Anywhere my favorite fruits lived was my preferred spot for lunch. There I would perch, eating until I was full "to the brim".

Going to "ground" with my grandfather on the weekends while my grandmother went to the market to sell her produce was a happy excursion for me. I could get as dirty as you can imagine and no one got upset with me. I carried yams, sweet potatoes, and dasheen, freshly dug from the earth to the basket. Papa cut the pumpkin from its vine and I carried it on my head.

I thought of my mother sometimes and wondered if she would come for me. I would give her all the mangoes that I piled into the "pudding pan" and then we would sit on the veranda and eat until the juice ran down the side of our mouths and unto our clothes.

"Grandma save dis mango for mummy."

"Eat yu mango baby, yu madda nah come ya caah she nuh waa yu."

Each time my grandmother said those words my heart hurt. I didn't want to believe her, but grandma wouldn't lie to me. I thought about things I could do to make mummy want me. Since she wasn't around I helped grandma and grandpa with everything they needed. I wanted to be sure they liked me and wanted me.

One hot and hazy Saturday afternoon while my grandmother was at the market, and I was playing in the yard, my mother and sister showed up. I jumped for joy. My wish had finally come true. I ran inside to tell Papa.

"Mummy want me, si har here she come fi me."

Mummy looked pretty in her big sun shades, red blouse, and blue jean shorts. She told me she had been looking for me for a long time and that my father was playing games. She said if I'm not living with my father then I am to live with her. She said she wouldn't take me until my grandmother was home. She gave me my bath, combed my hair, and put me in a new pink and light green short set with a little vest she brought with her. Then we walked to the shop (outta road) to buy bun and cheese and "cheese krunchies".

My sister and I took a picture together, which helped to etch that memory into my heart. That is still my favorite outfit of all times and one of my favorite memories.

When my grandmother came home, my grandfather told her what had happened. She left the house hurriedly and went to the "shop" to make a phone call to my dad. A few days later my dad came and he and I left my grandmother's. I thought for sure I was going back to my mother. We traveled deep in the country to a place where I had never seen before and a place I couldn't even imagine that people lived. This journey brought me to live with my father's sister. She looked like a tall brick wall and I had to look up with my head tilted back on my neck when I spoke to her, just like I had to do when talking to my dad. She said she ran a chicken farm.

She did not greet me with a hug or a smile. She just spoke directly to my father and matter-of-factly stated that she didn't care how old I was. If I was going to stay there, I was going to wake up the same time she and her husband woke up and I had to be willing to work.

"How old are you?" I barely opened my mouth to answer when she continued speaking. "You going to have to help out, we don't have use for no babies on this farm." She said, as she bent over and slapped an annoying mosquito from her knee. Her motions and suddenness frightened me and made me jump with the sound of her hands hitting her legs. "Mosquito." She said, without any hesitation.

My father convinced her that I was a good helper. "Ask mam. She ongly look likkle bit, but she trong."

It was late and she was already in her night clothes. "Take up your bag. You sleeping in that room she pointed. Go put on your nighty. You have to get up early in the morning and help." She declared. She motioned my dad to a corner and they did more talking, but this time in whispers.

My aunt and her husband raised brown and white chickens in a large coop. The coop was made of wood, but it had wire lining along the front and bottom portions. The top was completely closed and that's where the chickens came to roost. I had to let them out in the mornings. They walked out briskly and some eager ones flew. Once they were out, it was my job to look for eggs. I picked them up and brought them in the kitchen. Then, I would spread their feeds all around as they rushed to pick some more. Afterwards, I took a bath in a silver wash pan and got ready for school. In the evenings I helped to clean the coop, gave chickens fresh water, packed them back in the coop, and swept up the yard, all before the orange sunset. The chickens were all loud and filthy. No matter how fast or hard I worked, there was still more work to do. I wanted to go home.

Going to church with my aunt and her husband was a respite, as my Sunday School teacher had a nice smile and she was kind. She always told the Sunday School class that if we believed in God, anything we prayed for would be delivered to us. Every day no matter where I was, I prayed that I would soon go back to my Mummy.

Whenever I wasn't taking care of the chickens, I played lots of games by myself to keep me from boredom. "Eeny meeny miny moe" with my feet was my favorite. I also played court and the judge. My court always decided I would go back to my mummy. One musky Saturday afternoon, a man who worked in the town of Mandeville came to tell us that my mother was in Mandeville and she was waiting to see me. My aunt told him that she had indeed made arrangements to take me to see her, but I wasn't going until I finished all my chores.

I couldn't believe that she didn't tell me I was going to see my mother. I worked so hard the rest of that day, trying to do everything right so that my aunt wouldn't find any excuse not to take me to see my mom. Every chore Aunty inspected needed to be done over. By the time I finished my work and we drove the unpaved rocky roads back to Mandeville, (which was more than 50 miles away from the bushes where we lived), it was dark and my mother was nowhere in sight. I pressed my forehead up against the window of the old blue truck and cast my eyes around every woman, looking hard for one that resembled my mother. As the truck drove off and headed back for the country, I felt so guilty for not working fast enough and not being diligent enough the first time. I cried as if I had been whooped.

A few more years passed with me working on the chicken farm. One year while I was on summer vacation, my aunt told me to get dressed and pack my things. I was going to Kingston to see my mother. Yes! God was answering my prayers! I was leaving that shitty place with those nasty chickens and finally going home. I hurriedly packed all my things in a bag and when Aunty told me to put the chickens back in the coop, I shove and kicked them in quickly. I was ready to go home. As I threw everything I owned in a bag, I felt like I was getting ready to collect an award. I was so happy.

When I got to Kingston, everything was perfect again. My Mummy had gotten remarried, and she had a new baby. Helping her with the baby was fun and my mom couldn't believe how much I'd grown or how caring and helpful I was. Of course I piled on the help and Mummy didn't have to lift a hand. By now I had learned to cook and clean house, so I cooked every day for Mummy and her new family.

One day while we all sat down to eat at the dinner table Mummy said that she was so sorry that I was only spending the summer. I couldn't believe what I heard or that this was happening to me. "I have to go back to that God forsaken place they called a farm? Deep in the middle of a jungle?" I asked. I told her that I didn't want to go back because all I did was work and no matter how much I worked, the work was never done. I was so disappointed that my mother was sending me away again. I stopped talking to her for the rest of my visit and I also stopped cooking for her and her family.

It was hard for me to enjoy the rest of my summer break with my Mummey and sisters. I spent the rest of the summer always in a quiet corner or hidden under the bed. I didn't know when I would have to leave and that thought worried me every day. My grandmother was right. Nobody wanted me. Those words haunted me. I tried to make them go away, but they kept coming back. *I don't know why nobody wants me. I'm a good child. I always have manners. I'm smart and I get good grades.*

When it was time for me to go back to the chicken farm, I couldn't find my favorite pair of shoes that Mummy bought me. She accused me of hiding it so that I wouldn't have to leave. She told me when she found it she would come look for me and bring it. The ride back to the country was one of the most painful trips I have ever taken. Why would Mummy let me go back to this horrid place?

When I got back to the farm, I was very quiet. I hardly spoke to anyone and I yelled at the chickens. I became even quieter than I had been before I left for Kingston and I stayed out of everyone's way. I went back to playing my quiet games and playing judge. This time the judge would rule that I go back to live with my grandparents. I knew now that I was lucky they kept me in their home and even though I wasn't glad to do my chores, I did them with pride, even when I yelled at the chickens. A few months after my trip to Kingston my aunt told me to get dressed because my mother wanted me to take passport pictures.

"Passport pictures, fi what?"

"Yu madda going to farin and she taking you with har. Yu going home."

I let out a deep breath.

The time I spent away from my mother left a deep hole in my heart. I always felt like I didn't belong at her family gatherings. I haven't felt as if I am as much her child as my other two sisters who were always with her. Now that I have my own family, I give my children individual quality time and I thank God that their circumstances are different from mine." Tasha spoke with such passion.

***

After she finished her story, Eva walked over to her and hugged her. Then, she gently released her and ran both her hands down Tasha's arms to her hands. She held her hands and asked, "Where are you now?"

"Well, shortly after I left the farm, I came to New York with my mother. I was thirteen years old. By the time I was eighteen, I moved out. I wanted to date and have more freedom. I had a good career as a shopper for Sax Fifth Ave. I am married now and have two beautiful children. I am happy."

"Are you still craving your mother's love and approval?"

"Yes."

"How?"

"I jump at her beck and call and I rarely ask for her help with anything."

"Why?"

"I want her to see that I appreciate her, but also that I am independent and smart."

"What do you have to do to get your mother's love and approval?"

"I have to forget all the things I've been through when I'm around her."

"Why?"

"Because when I ask her questions about what happened when I was young, she gets angry and she shuts down."

"How does that make you feel?" Eva asked, as she tilted her head in concern swaying her soft locks.

"I feel like saying, 'how fucking dare you leave me for so many years and not want to talk to me about it!'"

"What if I told you that your mother also desperately craves your love and acceptance? And her shutting down and getting angry is because she hates herself just like you do for not having done more for you? What if you were to call your mother and thanked her for everything you have been through and also for the strong accomplished woman you are today?"

"That would be hard."

"Why?"

"Because I always thought that I did everything by myself, for myself."

"Okay, so the feelings that you have about creating a happy stable family and giving individual attention to your children; where did that come from?"

"That came from me not wanting my children to live in uncertainty with people who are cold towards them."

"That," Eva started, "came from your experience, which you hold your mother responsible for. So, if you're going to hold your mother responsible for the bad things that happened in your life, then you have to hold her responsible for the good things in your life. Thank her for all the good in you and the good decisions you've made. Your homework is to have a heart to heart with your mother which should start with, "I thank you for all that I am…" Eva continued, "You name all the good in you, one by one. You are good enough Tasha, and she is responsible for that."

Rory's Story
Voices

I hear voices. Sometimes I hear them when I sleep, but other times I hear them when I'm wide awake. The voices are usually loud and clear, but sometimes they're not. They are muffled, indistinguishable, or hauntingly quiet. Some voices are more dominant than others and when they are present it is harder for me to be. I live in a dream and I dream while I'm awake. When I do fall asleep, I'm always on the run in my recurring dream; running very fast through a tightly wooded area - moist, damp, and gloomy. I'm breathless and the force of the darkness of the night pushes against me. My mouth appears to be screaming, but no sound can be heard; only the sound of my footsteps running, running, running after me. The wind is cold, strong, and piercing. It hits my face and I feel the wetness from my eyes burn into my skin. Suddenly, I'm awake.

I'm happiest when I know I'm wide awake, so I stay awake for as much as I can. I stay awake enough to get the coveted job, join a church, marry the guy I trusted with my heart, buy our dream home, and have two beautiful children. The voices are not all intimidating. Some are loving and kind, but some are loud, forceful, and frightening. I work from home mostly and I'm glad to have this option, because it's harder for me to concentrate in public spaces. There are too many voices vying for my attention. Some voices I quickly recognize. They immediately put a smile on my face and give me a warm feeling, like the feeling I got when I would hear my mother's voice singing along to her favorite album. She would belt sweet gospel music early in the morning. She had a beautiful voice. I miss that voice.

My mother was a woman of few words, but when she did speak it was magnetic. Even in disciplining me her voice was rough but so sweet, like a spoonful of honey or sugar in your mouth. She had brown skin and a big Jheri curl afro.

From where I was standing, she was tall and sturdy. She used to wash my hair every Saturday then made "bantu knots" or what my sister Rachelle called "chiney bumps" with it. On Sunday mornings, she undo the knots from my hair, and I would have curly hair for church.

I wore beautiful dresses with frills or flowers and pretty lace stockings or socks to church. Our church was Macedonia Baptist Church. It sat directly across the street from our house. From Mommy's room you could see the high steeples perched on the top of the red-bricked walls. I had two older brothers and a baby sister who lived with us, but Mommy told us that she had five other children when she lived in Jamaica and they were our older brothers and sisters. On Sundays, we walked across the street to the church, hand in hand while she hipped my baby sister. My two older brothers would run ahead of us. At times she would have to call out to them to slow down or to stop and not kick at anything in their Sunday shoes.

She sang in the church choir and when it was her time to sing, she would give us all peppermint or ginger candy that we knew was stashed in her purse. After church, we waited until Mommy hugged and kissed almost all the church members, especially the ones who seemed older than God himself. We walked back across the street to our home for Sunday dinner, which mommy had usually already prepared before we went to church.

Once we got back in the house from church, we knew the routine; take off our Sunday clothes, put them away, put on "yard clothes" and wash our hands for dinner. We sat down to eat amongst laughter and the aroma of traditional Jamaican Sunday dinner: rich rice and peas, brown stew chicken, with cabbage and carrots finely cut, or a salad of lettuce, carrots, tomatoes, cucumbers, and Mommy's favorite, dried cranberries. Sometimes our cousins that lived downstairs came up for dinner. The bigger ones teased us and played games to distract us while our food disappeared from our plates. Mommy would laugh at us and remind us to always pay attention.

One Sunday morning, Mommy said we were not going to church because she had a surprise for us. She and her husband Milky left early that morning. I was playing on the porch with my brothers and my big cousins from downstairs when Mommy returned. She eased out of the car with a skinny legged girl. "This is Rachelle. She is your big sister." Mommy said excitedly.

Rachelle was tall and thin. She didn't smile. I jumped up to give her a hug after my cousin Katherine gave her a hug. Everyone appeared to be happy about Mommy's surprise, except the surprise. She walked cautiously around with Katherine, as she showed her the house. Then Katherine gave her a ragged doll and a smile surfaced on her dim face.

In the days that followed, Rachelle's quietness was put on pause when she spent time talking with my brothers and me. We were excited to have a big sister and we showed her around. We took her to our favorite park, the corner store, and we showed her off to our neighbors. Gradually, she started to smile. She helped us get ready for school in the mornings and was always there when we got home. She helped the boys with homework, and Milky helped us all with our school art projects. Milky was quiet, so Rachelle was in charge when Mommy was not at home.

Mommy always came home on Friday evenings or early Saturday mornings while we were still asleep. We knew she was home when we heard the thumping of the laundry bags and her asking Rachelle, what chores she had completed and what she needed to have done before she returned from the laundry mat. Saturdays were busy with cleaning the house and getting our hair pre-ready for church on Sunday.

Mom and Rachelle washed our hair and "chiney bump" it (bantu knots). When evening came, Mom put the red peas in a pot of water to soak overnight getting it ready for the rice and peas dinner. We spent all of Sundays together, getting into each other's way, telling mommy what happened while she was at her "live in" job, and making sure we got her attention before Monday morning. When we woke up on Mondays, Rachelle was back in charge until Friday evening or Saturday morning when Mommy was home at last.

One day Rachelle brought home a baby boy and told us we were aunties and uncles. He had the biggest, most beautiful eyes. He brought laughter to Rachelle's face and into our home. Our days were filled with us, our voices, our songs, and our quarrels.

Those days abruptly came to a halt, and so did our routines. One day after doing our laundry, my Mommy left with my cousin Katherine and her mom to go to a wedding. She was wearing a soft peach dress, the same color of her skin. It had a black belt cinched around her waist and big bow rested on her hips. Her afro was parted on one side and she wore red lipstick.

She lined us all up, Rachelle and her baby, Raven, Ryan, my sister Ruby and me and kissed us goodbye. I remember looking at the stain on my cheeks when she left. I told Rachelle I want to keep it, so she placed a napkin on my face and pressed softly. When she showed me the imprint of mommy's lips on the napkin I couldn't stop smiling. I can't remember seeing Mommy ever again.

I must have looked everywhere in that house for her. When I didn't hear the thumping of the laundry bags, I looked for her in her room. I saw Milky, sitting at the side of the bed with his head hanging down on his chest and his hands rested on his lap, still and quiet.

We lived on the third floor. There was Mommy's room, the kids' room, the living room, the kitchen, and a bathroom. She wasn't there. I looked on the second floor and she was not there. I looked on the first floor in the living room, in the dining room, in the kitchen and in the basement where the big cousins slept. She wasn't there either. I started to listen for her voice everywhere I went, yet, it wasn't there.

After she was gone, I remember my other brothers and sisters from Jamaica coming to live with us. I remember big bus trips in the summer to Dorney Park filled with laughter and excitement. Thinking back, I loved those times. I loved hearing those voices. I remember summer days in the park learning how to twist plastic strings into a bracelet of many colors. I remember playing Double Dutch in the streets with the kids on the block. I remember the summer rain and the days passing. But I don't remember hearing my Mommy's voice.

Sometimes, I close my eyes and try to listen for the voice of my mother, singing, calling, quarrelling, but it's hard. My memory feels like a dream and in my dreams I hear children laughing and playing as I listen. I remember days before mommy disappeared. Mommy and I walking hand in hand to pick flowers from the neighbor's garden. Us talking and laughing. She'd touch my hair as we walk and say "what a beautiful head of hair." I listen to hear Mom's voice say those words again, or anything at all. Instead I hear. "Don't move baby girl, you might get burned."

"Don't trust him."

"Don't touch that. There is poison hidden on it."

"Don't listen to her. She is jealous of you and she wants your job."

"They're watching you."

I would stay still for a long time no matter where I was, until the voices told me it was safe. I am grateful for the voices, because I know they care. However, I miss the days when I didn't need them. They are silent when I drink.

My friend's mother said that my family is cursed. I heard her say it when I was sixteen years old. "Not only did her mother die, leaving behind nine children, three of her sisters already had babies and they are not much older than you." My friend's mother whispered to her daughter.

That day my friend and I went to the movies. "You're next to get jacked up with a baby," she said. "You'll never amount to nothing. You'll wind up pregnant just like your sisters. I can't be your friend anymore."

It became my goal to prove them wrong. Even though I heard their whispers and their voices say those words all day long. I learned that a quick drink tuned them out and I listened to my inner voice instead. I learned at an early age not only to be quiet, but of the importance of listening. I listened more than I spoke.

Mr. Brandon was the first voice I heard. He says mean things like "eat shit", however, he also has told me when I'm in danger and shows up whenever I'm afraid. I've learned that if I stay still when he's ranting he will go away faster. A sip of wine usually helps. I've never had to do anything Mr. Brandon told me to do, not even when he cursed me and called me names. I just become still, listen keenly, have a drink and then he goes away.

He's been with me since I was thirteen. The first time he revealed himself to me, I had just been held down by a family friend who tried to rape me. The friend came in the house asking for one of my older male cousins. When I told him that no one else was there but me, he asked to use the bathroom. When he came out of the bathroom he pushed me up against the wall in the living room and tried to kiss me. I was so shocked I think my heart stopped and I froze. He pulled down my jeans, laid me on the floor, and pinned me there. I heard my voice trying to scream, but it sounded more like I inhaled it. He then pressed his arm across my neck while his other hand was taking off his pants. I heard him say, "Don't fight. You'll like it once it goes in."

Just then, one of my little cousins walked in along with my older cousin Jessica who had come home from college on holiday break. Immediately the family friend jumped up and ran. Jessica picked me up off the floor and asked me if I was okay. I coughed and coughed, nodded yes, and we never spoke of it again.

I heard a male voice call out my name in a whisper that night, but I was in the bathroom and I was alone. When I came out of the bathroom, I looked everywhere for a male in the house, but no one was there but me. Being alone became very difficult, so I would stay at the neighbor's house if no one else was home with me. I would always hear that voice saying, "Don't fight you'll like it once it goes in." I would also hear that quiet voice whispering my name. Eventually his whispers became louder and one day he told me his name.

When I was sent to live with my father, Mr. Brandon was angry and he didn't speak to me in whispers. He was loud and bold and he told me to do bad things. I never did. He knew things that happened before my mother disappeared and he would remind me of those things. He reminded me that my mother always said, "No matter what you do, don't ever send her to live with her dad." I ended up there anyway.

While I was there, I met someone and I called him my boyfriend. Mr. Brandon did not like him and he stayed away most of the times. That boyfriend raped me one day and Mr. Brandon blamed himself for staying away. He promised me he'd never go away for long ever again. He told me to hurt my boyfriend, but I ignored him. Instead, I tried to stay away from the house as much as possible and spend more time by myself. I would walk through the streets of Manhattan in a daze. Trying to figure out who to tell. I believed that if I told anyone what happened I would hear their voice say, "You brought this on yourself."

"Why would you trust some boy you hardly knew?"

"This is all your fault." Mr. Brandon blamed me, but he also blamed himself for not being there.

When I couldn't find anyone in my father's house I trusted to tell what happened to me, I stopped eating. I made a conscious decision not to eat so that my dad and step-mom would decide to send me back to live with my family. I never wanted to see this rapist again. I didn't eat for days, but that didn't work. I stayed with my father until I left for college.

Even though Mr. Brandon was around more, I managed to keep him a secret. I managed to hear the voice of my family encouraging me to make something of myself. They told me to focus on going to college and getting a "good job". They had no idea the struggles I had to go through to focus just to hear what was going on around me.

While I was away at college in my first semester, another voice appeared. She said her name was Tis and that she was thirteen. Her voice was tender and soft, but she was brilliant and she knew things that a typical thirteen year old, or even I could have never known. She was also witty and logical. When Mr. Brandon called me mean names or told me to do mean things, she would tell me why I shouldn't listen to him and then recite powerful affirmation into my ear. She also knew statistics very well and she would tell me the probability of me getting into or out of trouble. So I opted to listen to her more. She told me things about the Bible and I started visiting a church near campus. I learned that God loves me, and he loves me more than my mother did.

I now understand more about what is true and real and that is: Nothing is as our Father God originally designed it. I was not promised a perfect life, nor, that I would grow up with my mother. I may get hurt, and that I may hurt others. No one is to be trusted. I hear voices, yet I am enough. I am passing through the world and nothing here is promised.

The Bible talks about how easy people can be swayed even with the word of God.

Mark 4:15-17: *Some people are like seeds along the path where the word is sown. As soon as they hear it, Satan comes and takes away the word that was sown in them. Others, like seeds sown on rocky places; they hear the word and at once receive it with joy. But since they have no root, they last only a short time. When trouble or persecution comes, they quickly fall away.*

What's guaranteed is that trouble and persecution will come. So, what am I to do about it? I had to learn that it was okay to not always have an answer. I learned that I needed to start listening for a new voice. The voice of someone who loved me unconditionally, someone who wanted the best for me, someone who "planned to prosper [me] and not to harm [me], planned to give [me] hope and a future. I had to start trusting that I didn't know what was best all the time. I had to believe that this life has meaning apart from those old voices that told me I couldn't or told me nothing at all. They never invaded my ear about the things a girl should know. I had to figure things out on my own.

I figured out that I could make a way for myself as long as I just went to school and got an education. Well, I did, and after completing my double major in four years, being paid more than I knew what to do with, buying "the" car, I still felt lonely. I often thought, is this what life is about?

I wanted to live a better life; a life without fear and mistrust. Church had a positive energy and I enjoyed the beautiful, loud singing. It drowned out Tis and Mr. Brandon's voice. Eventually, I sat down and studied the Bible with the ushers. I learned that I didn't need to be strong all by myself. That God wanted me to thrive, not just survive. I had to seek His voice, because he is my Father. It helped me throw off timidity and find the strength to conquer things in life that many are fearful of and things that many are still struggling with.

I had to listen to that voice within reassuring me, "Great things come to those who don't give way to fear." When I ended up getting married and tried to have children, we were still unsuccessful after eight years. I started to believe the voice of Mr. Brandon saying, "This is your fault. You caused this on yourself... This is a punishment from God for all the things you've done wrong." Instead of internalizing the voice, I had to fight to trust the Bible and my Father's words, "Never will I leave you, and never will I forsake you."

I learned to silence the voices in my head and listen for the whisper of the Lord. I learned to speak words of encouragement to myself, and to differentiate between the sounds of the voices in my head and the voice of God. As I read more of God's word, I learned more about his heart.

***

Eva was sitting directly across from Rory when she began to speak, but as Rory's story progressed she got up and sat in front of her. As Rory spoke, Eva leaned in so her face was almost in Rory's lap. When Rory finished telling her story, Eva hugged her and swooped her off the floor.

"You are perfect, just the way you are. A child needs a few things to grow and flourish," she said as she wiped the tears from her face. "Stability, love, and trust. It is as important as food and good shelter. Without them your mind will find ways to create that. The voices that have been following you like Mr. Brandon and Tis became a part of you because your mind felt the need to protect you."

Joy's Story
The Dream

It was the best day of my life. I wore my favorite dress; the one I wore to church on Wednesday nights for prayer meeting, but never on Sundays because there was a hole in it right by the daisy which sat in the middle of the neckline. It came to me like that. It was bright blue and the hemline stopped just a little bit above my ankles. My last birthday it was all the way below my knees. I remember because my birthday was on a Wednesday and as soon as I came home from school, I got dressed for prayer meeting. "Gyal where yu does going dress up like back foot?" Gran Gran asked. "I'm going to prayer meeting!" I declared as I spun like a gig. Gran Gran laughed so hard she said she wet her pants.

That birthday I twirled so hard while playing hopscotch in the yard. Every turn was a chance to display the flowing beauty of my dress. This beautiful dress I chose to wear to America because I felt lucky to have it, and happy whenever I wore it. I felt lucky going to America where I was going to live with my father, whom I have not seen for eight years. I remembered I had to wake up before dawn. It was so early, the sky was blue and black at the same time. Mummey woke me up to get ready for my long journey. By the time we walked from our zinc house to the gas station where we would get a taxi, the sky opened up to a beautiful mixture of many different shades of blue mixed with burnt orange and straw colored yellow.

The taxi had the word Airport spelled on both sides and we crammed in. It was so tightly packed, I had trouble squeezing in my backpack which was my only luggage. I sat on Mummey's lap in the back in the middle of the taxi. I counted seven of us in the back of the taxi and four in the front, including the driver. I prayed that my dress would survive this sardine can packing, but I knew from experience whenever I caught the taxi with my Mummey or Gran-Gran that they started out crammed, but didn't last long. The taxi took us on a long and bumpy ride through the town. I couldn't sit still, so I counted. I started with all the buildings with names on them, then all the blue cars, and then counted all the VW cars. Finally, we arrived at Piarco International Airport.

The airport was the biggest place I had ever seen in all my life. It had huge glass windows that seemed to start at the top of the building and stopped at the very bottom. The glass wrapped around the entire building. Posted in front of the building were giant flag poles with flags from all the countries in the world. Saluting us like brand new soldiers. We hopped out the taxi and Mummey held my hands very tight under her arms while she paid the driver.

"Don't move gyal, ole yu bag." Mummey said hurriedly.

I grabbed my bag and quickly mounted it on my back. When inside the airport, the super shiny floors boasted a superior luxury even more beautiful than the Lilac Inn I could have imagined in Nancy Drew's "The Mystery of the Lilac Inn".

Mummey walked with me to the counter and explained to a very pretty lady with even prettier white teeth, why we were there. She then gave my big white envelope to the smiling beauty. The woman told Mummey she could stay with me until I boarded the flight. Mummey walked with me to the landing and held my hand all the way. "Gyal yu must listen to yu farder. Do yu school work, bade yu skin clean, wash yu panty as yu tek it aff, help clean di house; show yu farder yu have good use." Mummey's brown nose turned red and her eyes filled with water. She hugged me and suddenly all my excitement turned to disappointment. I had been so excited about going to America that I forgot Mummey wasn't coming with me.

It was all her fault for getting me so excited about the trip in the first place. She told me if I went to America, I would be able to come back anytime I wanted *"as long as school out"*. She told me if I went to America, I could get a job as a babysitter when I turned thirteen, and I would be able to buy pretty clothes, stockings, and broad hat fi Gran-Gran and send har money fi build a house. No more zinc house, "Allo'we gon have more fi do wid life cause a yu mi gyal." Mummey caroled these sayings every day, always gleeful and always smiling. Not once did I ever glimpse the pain she now shows. This pain that stood boldly in front of my unseeing eye, almost like a warning of what was to come.

My heart felt so heavy and I didn't want to ever leave her. I didn't want to leave Trinidad. As I looked at Mummey, I saw her smile through her tears. She said, "Allo'we gon have more life cause a yu, yu, going or not?"

I may have hesitated, but after I saw a glimpse of the future with a house made of cement blocks and a real roof with a veranda, I stopped crying. No more old rusty zinc house that rain came straight through on Gran-Gran bed. No howling wind to keep me up in the middle of a hurricane season. No more running to the church when the storm was threatening to blow off the zinc roof or after it actually did. "Yes I'm going to America Mummey, and when I come back I gon build a house and put flush toilet in deh." I said. Mummey laughed.

"Concentrate yu mind pon u school work. I am happy for you chile. 'Nuff moder don't have my luck to see dem pickney get a chance at life. Mek something a yu self. Listen to yu fader." Mummey said. My name was called over the loudspeaker and a prettier lady than the one before gestured me to come to her. "You are going on the flight first darling, come with me." She stated, as she smiled.

On the flight, I ate so much I felt sick. I didn't know what to do with myself and the uncomfortableness in my stomach, so I went to sleep. By the time I woke up it was time to land and one of the pretty flight attendant with green eyeshadow to match her uniform directed me to open the window shade. A beautiful and sunny baby blue sky rose up to greet me. I was in America.

When I walked off the airplane at Miami International Airport, the sunlight sparkled on the wide window pane and bounced off of my eye lids. I saw my father through the beams of light. His shadow appeared to me before I saw his body. He was directly behind another person and I noticed his shadow on the wall to the right of his body. He stood tall through the crowd and behind the waist high barricade. It was there I saw him for the first time in years. I waved shyly not knowing what to expect, or how he would great me. The flight attendant walked me over to him and they exchanged a few words. "Here Sir, are her papers and this backpack is her only luggage." She said. My father playfully slapped me on my shoulder with the papers and with a wide open eye he said, "Welcome to Merca."

We walked out of the airport, his hand holding mine and into a sea of yellow cabs, cars, and buses. When we got to the parking lot my father told me I was too small to ride up front with him, so I sat in the backseat with my backpack. He showed me how to buckle myself in the seat belt and off we went, driving into the beginning of my future. The car smelled like when the rainfall leaked through the roof and into Gran-Gran's church shoes. He asked me some questions on the way, but I mostly just looked out the window.

The place looked unbelievably magical and I felt like a superhero gliding past extremely tall buildings and colorful lights. I had never seen such wide roads in all my life and the cars were moving so fast I couldn't even count them all. Then there were the golden arches that read McDonald's; they were everywhere. *McDonald must be the prime minister of this place*, I thought to myself.

We pulled up to a beige bungalow with a driveway and a big front door. It was dark outside, but the house lights were already on when we got there. "Your home gyal, jump out on my side." He said. *My father must be rich*, I thought. This was the biggest house anyone I knew had. When I walked through the doors I didn't know what to do with myself. On the left there was a big black couch, a big tall television stood in front, and a short table sat in between the couch and television. On one side of the room was a fish tank. You could look at the television in front or at the fish to the right. Next to that room was a kitchen with a refrigerator, stove, and a small table in the corner. When you walked past the kitchen there was a small room with a bed and night stand. The bed had on a pink spread like a big pink bubble gum. "That be your room gyal, check it out no." My father said. Back dere be my room, you stay in your quarters and I stay in mine.

I went in and sat on the bed and my dad brought in my backpack and placed it on the carpeted floor. I was in total disbelief that this will be my life. I had never been in a house so huge. My father had to be rich. That night, I stayed up crying and missing my mother and Gran-Gran. I felt guilty that I was in America in this beautiful home and they were in Trinidad. I wished they could've been there with me.

My first night in my new home, my father told me to call him Rocky. I didn't feel comfortable with that so I told him let your friends call you Rocky and I will call you what I been calling you all my life, Papa. Immediately life got busy and my days were filled with doctor's appointments and registering for school, the YMCA for after school, and swimming for Saturdays. By the time I started school I was just happy not to be on the road running around with Papa. He was always frustrated and upset that he had forgotten something or he had to go somewhere else for an important paper, or to get something notarized. His frustration annoyed me.

I started school in grade six. It was so different in America compared to my school in Trinidad. The teachers talked so low in their throats you could hardly hear them, and the students talked so funny I couldn't make out what they were saying. They laughed every time I spoke and asked me to repeat everything I said. I hated school. It wasn't long before the teacher called my papa and told him that I looked sad.

"Joy, how's school?" He asked.

"School is alright papa." I said.

"Teacher say yu no look too happy."

"I don't know how to be happy in dat school."

"What yu mean?" He asked. "What is making yu sad, yu miss yu madda?"

"I miss she papa, but I don't sad fi she when I deh school." I answered.

"So what is di matter gyal?"

"Di students, dem laugh mi papa. Everyting I sey is joke fi dem. I tun laughing stock fi dem, and di teacher don't talk up 'tall. I can't hear noting she say."

"Fix yu face in class man. Is you duty to try, cause you is in dem country." He said.

Next day I remembered what papa said while I was in school and I tried to smile more. When class was over the teacher said we needed to talk.

"Yes teacher."

"Don't call me teacher. My name is Mrs. Rothenstein. Is that hard for you to say?" Her voice still lingered in the back of her throat.

"No ma'am." I replied.

She continued to say I looked uncomfortable in her class after a week and that she was worried that I either wasn't paying attention or I just didn't understand her.

"Teacher-," I began, but quickly rephrase my sentence. "Mrs. Rothenstein... I am trying to pay attention, but your voice don't come all the way to my chair in the back."

"Oh you can't hear me? You should have said that! Tomorrow, I will move you up to the front of the class." She then gave me a big hug and said, "I thought you didn't like me. You were back there making all those faces." She laughed and I just smiled because she was moving me up to the front of the class.

The next day I sat next to Jolene Brown. She looked just like her name; brown and pretty with golden skin that glistened with Vaseline. Jolene would reach into her bag and grab her clear lipstick, wrapped her fingers around it, and dragged it across her pouty lips. At break time she said "Hi!" and gave me a chewing gum. Then, she taught me how to make popping sounds with my bubble gum. We sat together for lunch that day. Ever since then we had lunch at the same lunch table and ate the same things every day. After school we walked home together and on weekends Jolene's cousin Grace would braid our hair. Then she would take us to "movie marathon". The "movie marathon" is where you pay for one movie and when it is over, you sneak in to another movie without paying. While we were at the movies, Grace would spend time with her boyfriend. We did this until Grace and her boyfriend came back to pick us up.

The next year we went to seventh grade together and joined the track team. We had track meets on Saturdays, so Sundays was the only day we didn't spend together unless we were getting our hair braided. On Sundays I stayed home, cleaned up the house, and went with Papa to the supermarket; Jolene went to church with her family. I wrote letters to my Mom and Gran-Gran back home and sent them money from my allowance. Mummey wrote me back to say what she was doing with the money I sent her. She bought a battery powered radio and said she and Gran-Gran listened to it all day. She was saving some money to buy new zinc to fix the roof. I read the letter Mummey sent me to Papa and he said to ask her how much more she needed to buy the zinc. By the time I was finished grade seven, Papa sent a big barrel to Mummey and Gran-Gran with clothes, canned foods, bags of rice, flour, and a big bottle of oil. Mummey put new zinc on the roof, and set it up so water can drain off the roof and into an empty drum. Mummey was very happy for that because now she didn't have to walk to the community pipe to collect water. Mummey wrote in her letter:

Gyal,

I living big down here. My roof shine like a willy penny and I walk roun aback go ketch wata like I a rich smaddy. All who neva give me no wata before, naw get none from mi. Anyway, I hope you are doing yo school work. Don't fret yo'self about me and Gran-Gran. Mek sure yo listen to yo fada and please keep di place clean. I raise you good so do good.

With love,

Your Mother. (Written by Ashley, ya neighba; send somting nice fa mi nuh)

***

Very poor people, like my family, had to share a community water pipe, which was located at an inconvenient distance from our home. Sometimes you ran out quicker than you expected and you would have to beg your neighbors. Not having to do so upgraded our status in the community. Instead of begging for water, others could now ask Mummey or Gran-Gran. Now, she could just go in her backyard and catch water from her own barrel just like the people in our community back home that were better off.

Jolene lived three blocks away from my house so we walked to school together. One day while I was in school my throat felt dry and it started to burn me. I told Jolene and at lunch time she walked me to the nurse's office. The school nurse checked my temperature, looked down my throat, and called my Papa to pick me up and take me to see my doctor. I left school in the middle of the day. Papa took me to the doctor and the nurse swabbed my throat with a big cotton Q-tip and then told me I had strep throat. I was out of school for the rest of the week. That was the only time I missed school.

Even though I was sick, Jolene came to my house every day to check on me. We watched BET and danced to Destiny Child's Independent Women. We used my brush and a comb for our mics as we danced and jumped all over the living room. When Usher came on with "U Remind Me", we fell to the floor. Usher made us weak. Then Puff Daddy and Jay Z came on with "Do You Like It" and we were definitely back on our feet dancing to their slick moves. But when Bow Wow came on, we just screamed and lost our minds.

My Papa drove us to our track meets on some weekends and Jolene's parents took us on others. Jolene and I won many races. Although I was faster than her in the 200 and 400 meter race, I could never beat her in the long distance races. At the end of the school year, there was an award ceremony and I received the math and home economic award along with a big trophy for track. My Papa stood up and shouted and clapped. When I went to accept my award, Papa shouted, "Joy don't move!" and he took a picture of me with all my awards while I was on the stage. I was so embarrassed. On our way home Papa said he was going to send the picture to my mom and Gran-Gran. He then had a poster size print developed, and hung it in our living room.

The summer after seventh grade, I turned thirteen on August 30th. That day was the worst day of my life. Jolene was away on vacation with her family. It had been the usual regular Florida weather; hot all month long, averaging anywhere between ninety to one hundred degrees. However, on that August day it was unusually cold and foggy with inconsistent heavy rainfall. Papa said we would go for ice cream when he came home from driving his taxi. I laid on the couch and watched BET until he got back.

Papa came home early and brought vanilla ice cream for me. He said it was too nasty outside to take me out, and there was a storm coming. Papa also said that it was too slow and there were not many customers out there. After I ate my ice cream with Papa, he said we could have a drink (I had never had a drink before) and he gave me one shot of whatever he was drinking. It burned my throat, so when he went to lay down in his room, I went to the living room to watch TV. I fell asleep listening to the thundering rain and watching Degrassi High.

That night, I had a dream. I dreamed I was alone in a gigantic warehouse. It was dark and empty and had no windows, only one giant door. I saw a big puddle of water in the middle of the room. I heard the heavy rain and the angry sound of the wind. I looked around to see if I could find the source of the water and to find a hiding place from the angry wind. As I walked to the far right hand corner of the room, someone held my hand and said, "This way, Joy."

I saw me in the corner of the room clothed in a majestic white gown with a cape made of feathers. The feathers were attached from the hood of the cape which covered my head. In the front of the hood, covering my forehead, I had a crown of silver. As I stood in the corner, people started to come into the warehouse and walk towards me. To the left of me was a huge oblong rattan basket filled with different kinds of bread. To the right of me was another rattan basket. That one was even bigger, about the size of a table. It displayed all sorts of fruits and vegetables.

I recognized some of the people walking towards me. Some I knew very well from back home, like the principal of my primary school; but others I couldn't recognize at all. All of them bowed in front of me and then I reached into the basket on my left and gave them bread and fruits and vegetables from the basket to my right. As I distributed the rations, a man dressed in all black, with a long black robe and long train about two feet, slithered his way pass the crowd.

As he walked, he dragged the rain water with him. He and the puddle stopped right in front of me. The crowd stood aside and gave him complete access to me. Everyone in the crowd bowed their heads. No one looked up as he marched up to me, scooped me up in his arms, threw me over his shoulder and carried me out.

When I woke up I was in my father's bed. I was confused because I had never slept in my father's bed before and I couldn't remember leaving the living room. I felt pain in my underwear and it was wet and slippery. My father was not in his bed when I woke up and I thought I must have walked in there by mistake. But how would I explain to him that I messed his bed? I'd never wet my bed before. I looked under the covers and it was blood. I tried to get up, but the pain in my private wouldn't let me and my head was spinning. I got sick and all I could think was that Papa raped me, but I couldn't remember. You would have to have a lot of nerve to rape your own daughter.

There was no more rain that day or angry wind and Papa was not at home. I got sick while I was taking a shower and vomited all over the bathroom. I didn't have the strength to clean it up, but I knew I had to before he got home because I messed his bed up and now I messed the bathroom, too. My mind was racing. I didn't know what to do. If Papa raped me I couldn't stay there anymore. I had to go back home to my Mom and Gran-Gran.

That evening when Papa came home his eyes avoided mine. He asked me if I was okay and I told him it burned when I peed. He said, "Yu a big girl now. Sometimes those things happen." He didn't sound too concerned and that worried me more.

I wrote a letter to my mom and told her what I think happened. I told her I wanted to come home. When Jolene and her parents came back from their family vacation, it was time to get ready for back to school and they took me shopping with them. Papa gave me my own shopping money and Jolene's mother helped me pick out clothes. She was very attentive to me and she noticed that I looked like I had a lot on my mind. She was beautiful and tall. Her left shoulder leaned a little and pointed up to her left ear. Her face was soft and caring and I wanted to tell her. Then she broke the silence saying, "Your father takes such good care of you." So I said nothing. I knew he did take care of me, but I also thought he raped me. I just couldn't remember what happened.

It was time for me to get a physical check-up at the doctors. The nurse ask me if I had seen any blood in my underwear and I told her yes. She asked me how long ago and I told her. I told her I was sleeping and the blood was there when I woke up. She said, "Those things happen when you are this age. Soon you will start to see your period at least once a month." She said it may not happen every month because in the beginning when a girl just starts to get her menstrual it might skip a few months. She told me to always carry a maxi pad with me to school, because a period likes to surprise girls and if we are not prepared it would be a bloody mess.

I did not tell her I was in my father's bed. I was too ashamed, and I didn't tell her about the pain in my vagina. She told me I was developing and meeting my milestones very well for my age. When I came out of the doctor's office, Papa was in the waiting area looking like an eager dog waiting to be walked. He asked me what I told the doctors and I told him nothing. He relaxed his shoulders and looked comforted by that.

Papa acted like nothing happened. Although I couldn't remember clearly, I know something wrong did. I tried to avoid him as much as I could. That was hard in a two bedroom bungalow, so I stayed in my room whenever he was home or whenever I was expecting him to come home. One day after school, I was in the living room on the floor doing math and watching Degrassi High. Papa came home very early. I heard him put his things away, but I hadn't gotten excited to see him come home since the night of my birthday and the mystery of me being in his bed with blood and pain in my underwear.

I pretended not to hear him say, "Joy yu watching TV?" I heard him walking towards the living room and I knew he could see me, but I did not answer him. I wanted to get up and go into my bedroom, but it was too late. I heard him walking around and I felt him walking up behind me, but I said nothing. Then I felt him kneel down behind me and rest his head on my back. My body froze and the hairs on my neck stood up. I was afraid and I froze. He pressed his hands in my back and my chest hit the floor. Then, I heard him breathe hot air onto the nape of my neck. I felt his hardness on my body and tears rolled down my face. My voice trembled as I said, "Please don't do this to me Papa."

He said, "Don't move and it won't hurt."

I screamed, but my voice quivered and choked me instead. I tried to fight, but he was strong and I couldn't move. I said, "Papa if you do this to me, I will tell the doctor."

"No one will believe you, no one." He said and his voice disappeared. When he got up, I rushed into the bathroom and closed the door.

That evening my father told me to come out of the room to eat something he cooked for us and that we had to have a talk. We talked at the dinner table while he was opening the mail and eating bake with tamarind sauce. He did not look up at me when he talked and I couldn't take my eyes off of him. He told me that if I was going to live in his house it made no sense for me to resist him.

"I won't hurt yu." He said. "Look at your life. Look at what you have. Look how much you and me have done for your mother and you grandmother since you been here in America. You can continue to give them a good life gyal, if you stop fighting me. You can't stay here if you keep fighting this thing. I will not fight with yu." He said. His voice was both calm and rough.

"If you tell anybody this thing, they will not believe you. I am a good person and everybody including your mother and your granny knows that. If you tell anyone and they even act like they want to believe you, I will just send my police fren to kill yu madda and yu granny." He said nothing else and I couldn't believe the things that this man was saying to me. The hairs on my arms stood up, my nose was running, and my eyes filled with tears.

After he made his argument, I knew my life in America was over because I was not submitting to this. My mind was racing. I didn't know what to do or where to go. I thought about telling Jolene's mother, but I was afraid that she wouldn't believe me. I was also afraid of what would happen to Mama, Gran-Gran and me. I had nothing more to say to this man. I knew he was serious and I would have to plan my escape. As he opened his mail, talked and ate, I thought about how to go back home and get away from this nightmare.

That evening, I did not sleep. I sat up in my bed with a steak knife in my hand. I told myself, if he came in here I was going to pretend to comply and then when he least expected it, stab him in his big round belly. He did not come in my room and he did not say goodbye when he left for work the next morning. As I rummaged through my father's important papers for my passport, I thought about who could help me escape.

Jolene's cousin Grace braided our hair. She was still in high school, but she was smart and feisty. She always told us if anybody messed with us to tell her. I hoped maybe she would believe me. I called her when I got to Jolene's house and told her that I had an emergency and I needed to see her today. After school, I met Grace at Jolene's house. She knew by the look on my face that something was wrong. Immediately she told Jolene to stay in the living room and let us talk privately. We walked to Jolene's room and sat down on the edge of her bed.

At first I was really afraid and my mouth felt stuck together. I didn't know how to start or what to say. My heart was racing and I felt every beat through my chest. I studied Grace's face and she looked like I could trust her. So, when she reached out and closed her hands over mine, I opened up and told her everything. Grace cried with me and hugged me. She let me cry and drool snot on her shoulders. She told me that she was sorry that she hadn't noticed that I needed help before and that she was glad I trusted her to help me.

"I don't know how I can help," she said, "but tell me what you want me to do with this information and I will do my best to help you be in a place where you feel safe.

"The first thing we should do is call the police." Grace said.

"Please don't. I don't want people to know that this happened to me. I don't feel like being blamed." I whispered.

"Tell me what you want me to do." Grace said.

I told her that I wanted to go back home to my Mom and my Gran-Gran in Trinidad. Grace said she would find out the process and how much the ticket would cost and get back to me. Grace suggested that we tell Jolene's mom, but I was afraid to tell her. It turned out that Grace's mom worked at the airport and she knew someone that could help me. That night Grace came back to Jolene's house for me with a ticket to Trinidad. She insisted that she had to tell Jolene's mother what was going on.

Everyone was crying and everyone wanted to call the police, but I didn't want that. I just wanted to go home to a place where I felt love, back to Trinidad. Jolene and her mother and Grace and her boyfriend took me to the airport that night. I only had my book bag with my school books and the clothes on my back. Grace gave the flight attendant an envelope and Jolene's mother gave me some money for the taxi to take me to my Mummey's house from the airport. I boarded the plane. Once I arrived at Piarco Airport, it was early morning, but the sun was still hidden. I was cleared by customs and the customer service representative put me in a taxi.

The heat of Trinidad's sun pierced my skin and my eyes as the morning woke. The taxi let me off on the main road and I began the long walk down the red dirt road to the house. It was an early Saturday morning, but I didn't see anyone around yet. I walked the quiet walk back home reflecting on the days not too long ago when I used to walk this path back from water catching, school, and church. I was barefooted, wearing torn and tattered clothes. Now I was wearing leather sneakers, jeans, and a shirt, with bag full of books on my back. Those days, I remembered, were days I used to think about going away to "farin". I used to hear so many successful stories of people who went to farin and everything got better for their families back home. Knowing my father was there I used to pray that one day I would get the opportunity to go. I never imagined that "going to farin" would cause so much trouble.

When I reached closer to my Mummey's house, I saw the shiny rooftop, but the same old board house with the dirty mildew and sunburnt color paint. Mummey was sitting in the back on the steps with an aluminum wash pan washing some clothes. When I stepped around the corner of the house and Mummey's eyes met mine she almost collapsed. I think she thought I was a ghost. She stood up and called my name as if she was questioning her sight. "Joy?" She asked.

"Yes Mummey, is me."

"You alright? Yu fada all right?"

"Yes Mummey."

"So how you get here? Who bring yu here?"

"I tek de taxi. Mummey yu get my letter?"

"Nobody on the road on ya si yu come here"

"No Mummey, you get my letter?

"What letter Joy?"

"The letter I write yu tell yu seh I having problem with Papa?"

"What problem yu having?"

"You get di letter Mummey? I explain it all in di letter."

"No, I don't get no letter. What yu telling me?"

"I run way."

"What! Run way?"

"I can't live with Papa anymore."

"What yu mean, yu can't live with Papa anymore?" Mummy's voice was getting loud.

"Mummy, Papa tell me I gwan haffi sleep wid he. Papa raped mi Mummey."

Mummy dashed over the wash pan as fast as lightning and slapped me straight cross my face.

"Shut yu madda's cunt!" She said and started to slap me up in my head. I didn't know how to answer. I didn't know what she wanted to hear, so I just screamed as she hit me that I was not going back. That's when my Mummy grabbed my face and sank her teeth into my cheeks. I couldn't believe it. I had forgotten all about Mummy's heavy hand and never imagined she could be so upset at me. She had not seen me in over three years and I just told her that I was raped and this is how she greeted me.

By the time Gran-Gran made it outside to see what all the commotion was about, Mummey had me on the floor stomping me with her foot. When she heard her mother, crying out "lawd have mercy" she picked me up and threw me towards Gran-Gran. I staggered back on Gran-Gran and she lost her balance. We both fell on the floor, then Mummey picked up her wash pan with the wet clothes, and threw them at me and Gran-Gran as we lay on the floor.

"You cannot stay here! Gwane back to farin and face yu bakkle. Leave dis place now, leave!" She wailed as she pointed me out of the yard. Gran–Gran started to cry, "What going on, what going on?" She pleaded.

"This yu chile! She do so much fi yu in her young age, what yu doing to har?" Gran-Gran cried as she scramble up off of the wet floor.

"What happened to you my darling? Look yu face. Come inside, I clean yu up. What happened to yu?"

I couldn't say it again so I folded my arms and buried my face in them and bawled. Gran-Gran hugged me and said, "If you come here for something and you didn't get it, it is not di end of di worl. Joseph broders sold him because of jealousy and fear. Yu madda is fearful and she is giving yu away to di worl. But you my chile will live to be the savior for this family. Look how yu small and yu done mek life betta fi two big woman. You are a different breed of woman and you going to change di worl. I don't know if I gwane live to see it, but I will pray for it until I die. Go on my chile." She kissed the wound on my face and hugged me.

"She not coming back here to disgrace me. She haffi leave and galong back where she coming from," said my mother. Gran–Gran was crying, but she told me, "Call yu aunty. Yu fada have a sister live in Brooklyn, New York. Har name Chaleney, she have same last name as yu. Call har to help yu."

As I walked back up the red dirt road, I sobbed hard and quiet, as I tried to wipe or inhale the wetness that was running out of my nose. I tried not to look back but I wanted to see my mother one more time. I turned and looked just over my shoulder. There, down the lane was the little one room house with shiny zinc roof, my Gran-Gran still holding wet clothes in her hands watching me leave her sight. But no, my Mummey was not there. I remember that day like it was yesterday.

I took the taxi straight back to the airport and asked for the flight attendant who helped me on my way to Trinidad. Someone got in touch with her and, by 10 p.m., that night, I was back in Jolene's parent's home.

Eyes, swollen, heavy, red and burning, and the biggest headache ever. I must have cried the entire day.

When I came back to Florida, Jolene, her mother, and Grace picked me up from the airport and I lived with them until I went away to college. I never forgave my father for what he did to me. He stole my innocence. My mother still calls me to this day, to tell me what she wants; and I give her everything she asks for. Yet I still resent her. Every time she asks for something, I take it as the opportunity to tell her how hard I work. When she ask me how come I don't have any children yet, I tell her children need good parents and even better grandparents.

***

Eva walked over to Joy and hugged her without saying a word for almost five minutes. The tears seeped through Joy's closed eyes and then she began to sob. There wasn't a dry eye at the table. We had no idea that this strong successful woman had been through such trauma and pain.

When Eva finally spoke she said, "You did not deserve that. Not from your father and not from your mother. What you deserve is real, pure love and to feel protected and safe. I am sorry for your hurt and for your pain. Today, you are in good company. Everyone here loves you and we want nothing in return. My story is nothing compared with what you've been through, nothing. However, what I've been through has made me stronger and made me dig deeper to give more of myself. That did not come easy. Someone worked with me and loved me through the hurt and the pain. Where are you now and how do you cope? Where are you in in your life and whose love do you know is safe?"

"I am a social worker and I spend most of my time volunteering. I don't know any safe love and I am not interested in love. I will not put myself out there for someone to hurt me. I don't know if I could live through that. I enjoy myself, but I don't want a relationship." Joy stated. "What you deserve is to feel safe and protected, and I am going to give you the number to an incredible therapist that will work with you to understand how what you've gone through continues to impact your life." Eva responded.

DENISE NICHOLSON

Amy's Story
Grace on the Horizon

In the spring of 2008, I came to America with my track team to represent Trinidad and Tobago at an athletic event, called the Penn Relays. I got used to traveling around my island for track meets and seeing large crowds, but this track meet was unlike any other I'd ever witnessed. Standing outside the locker rooms and onto the stadium, known as Franklin's Field, the seat looked long and shiny. From the red turf to the horseshoe shaped stadium, this place was a wonderland. I didn't run as well as I wanted to do, but I did well enough to have talent scouts interested in me. One was an American coach who was interested in me training with his high school team for the junior Olympics. He spoke to my coach and wanted to speak to my parents. I made the call on coach's phone. I spoke to my mother first and tried my best to explain what I understood.

"Mommy, dere's anoder racing game coming up. I want try out fi it."

"Really?"

"Yes Mommy, di Junior Olympics."

"Okay?" she questioned.

"Mommy, I can't come back now if I going try out."

"Really Amy?" Mommy's voice sounded strange.

"Mommy, I want talk to Daddy."

"Listen, you done do weh yu go dere to do already."

"Yes Mommy, and I getting more opportunity."

"Not all dat glitters is gold, Amy."

"Mommy, I want talk to Daddy." I heard the worry in her heart, and I knew she would be thinking from an emotional place. Daddy got on the phone.

"Daddy, I do real good at the Penn Relays."

"Nice."

"I get opportunity to try out fi something bigger dan dat race."

"Yu rale good yu no."

"Yes Daddy."

"Which race next?"

"Di Junior Olympics Daddy."

"Hmmhmm"

"Daddy, yu hearing me clear?"

"I hearing yu rale good. Let me talk to Derby."

I gave the phone to coach Derby. He and my dad talked for a while. I knew my parents were nervous. It all sounded so rushed. I also knew that if my dad agreed then my mom would be okay with it. Coach Derby handed the phone back to me. "Listen Amy, I not going rush my tinking yu nuh. So don't get excited." Dad quarreled.

I thought about all the possibilities of me winning at least one race in the junior Olympics in America. Boy that would put Trinidad and Tobago's name in the news! After they talked to my parents, I heard my team's coach and the American coach working out where I would stay and how I would be cared for during the time I would be here in America. My parents finally told me that they agreed that I could stay and prepare for the July Junior Olympics. I had no idea that my parents would really agree, but they both new the world of track and field and knew the possibilities. My father told me he planned to visit me within the next two weeks.

I am the fourth child out of five for my parents, and the first girl. When any of our goats got loose, no one could catch a runaway goat like me. My mother always laughed and said that's why my father was so protective of me. After the three day event in Philadelphia, Pennsylvania, I went to stay with the American coach and his family in White Plains NY.

Coach was a tall dark skinned man with a bearded face that genuinely hid his expressions. He and his wife had two children, Lauren and Ruth. Both girls looked like their mother; only, she had very white skin and long red hair. Their white skin looked darker than hers and their red hair looked like Shirley temples. Lauren was nine years old and constantly moving, and Ruth was six years old who liked dragging around a fluffy pink blanket and sucking her thumb. Lauren was a cheerleader and very active, and Ruth just sucked her thumb. I was hardly there but when I was, it was like a quieter version of my family back home. No goats to chase though.

Training for the Junior Olympics began almost immediately. I went early in the mornings with coach to the high school gymnasium for weight training or rehab exercises, and then on the track for warm ups and hurdle drills later in the day. I worked out individually and with the team. It was tough but it taught me dedication and incredible focus.

"I met Joy at the first Junior Olympics." Amy looked over her shoulder at Joy and grinned.

"I beat her twice." She said as she flashed her two fingers like a peace sign. "In the 400 meters and in the 4 X 400 meters relays." Joy hissed her teeth.

Winning felt good because of the medals and the gifts. With every competition more opportunities came and the date for me to go back home got pushed further into the future. My father came to visit me often, but my mom stayed home to care for the rest of the family. While Daddy was visiting the last time, I asked him some questions.

"Daddy, how is it that I never see you travelling so often before?"

"Yu studying mi?"

"Not really."

"Yu used to run down all the goats?"

"No sir, only the ones that ran away."

"Okay."

I was not into dating like the other girls my age. All I wanted to do was win and make my family proud. By the time I was a senior in high school I was the girl to beat; the one that was sure to get a great scholarship for college or better yet the one that was training to make the American track and field Olympic team. My grades suffered a sudden dip and I needed help quickly. Coach and his wife Faith thought it was a good idea for me to get a tutor. I saw the tutor twice a week and my grades started to improve. As time got close for the tryouts for Team USA Olympics, my practice time increased and the time with the tutor also increased. My grades were in good standing again and I was working out hard as ever on the field; still dominating my races.

One day, on the 30th of May to be exact, I was on the track and I did some hurdle drills to warm up my hip flexors. Next, I did some high knees when an unexpected burst of heat came over me and I felt my heart pounding inside. I passed out. I could hear faintly someone calling me by my track name. "Legs! Legs! You okay? Wake up! Open your eyes!" I couldn't answer and I couldn't keep my eyes open. The next thing I knew, I woke up flat on my back in the nurse's office.

"Hey, look who's up?" It was coach. He looked worried.

"How ya feeling?"

"Fine."

"What happened out there?"

"I don't know. My heart just started racing and then I was out."

"Don't worry. An ambulance is coming to take you to the hospital. I just want to make sure you're well."

Okay." I nodded my head.

At the hospital, they checked my temperature, blood pressure, my heart rate and how fast I was breathing and said I was fine. "Your heart rate is elevated, but that could be because you're dehydrated." The nurse said. She inserted an IV into my vein, taped it, and filled up about five vials with my blood. Then she attached a large bag of of fluids to the IV.

She gave me a small cup with a lid and told me to pee in it. She left and came back holding something in her hand. "Only ten dollars if you feel like covering up hun." She said sarcastically, but with a smile. "These are surgical pants, they won't hurt ya."

I looked down at myself and suddenly realized that my tall, well-toned frame was walking around in the ER in athletic running shorts and a sports bra. I looked naked. "Thanks." I answered shyly.

I was awfully glad that someone said something, because I was used to walking around like that. I slipped on the blue paper pants the nurse gave me, and looked over at coach. He was pacing back and forth near the nurses station. A strange anxiousness was lingering on his face. I turned on my phone, took a picture of my arm with the IV, and updated my Facebook post. I noticed that I had 77 unopened text messages so I went straight to opening and reading them. I didn't respond to them, because they were mostly fellow students wanting to know what happened.

"I hear your at the hospital, let them check out your heart. My brother passed out last year and they found a hole in his heart."

"Legs you good?"

"I heard, call me."

I stopped reading after the third message and sent a text in response to the last text I opened.

"So far so good, ttyl or maybe I'll see ya."

Two hours later I was still waiting for the lab results. It felt like I was waiting to start a big race. I didn't know why coach looked so worried. The doctor said my vitals were good, my heart rate was a little bit high, but he wasn't concerned and he said he would discharge me after the results of the labs come in.

When the results came in the doctor said he wanted to talk to me privately. He drew the curtains when coach stepped out. "Your results are in and you do not have any infection. In fact your labs are perfect and you are pregnant." I gasped, "What?!" My phone fell right out of my hand.

That had never even crossed my mind. I could not believe what I had just heard. My menstruation was always on and off. It might come three times a year maximum, so when I do menstruate is more of a surprise than when I don't. My mind started racing and my father's last visit instantly replayed in my head. Coach and Faith had told him that I had a boyfriend and he flew in from Trinidad to speak to me. I didn't tell him because my father was very strict and extremely focused. I knew he would overreact. He would view me having a boyfriend as a distraction.

When he arrived, he did not get angry like I expected, but he took me outside on the deck for a long private talk. We sat at the patio table; him at one corner and me at the head of the table. He had a cold beer in his hand and he asked me if I was having one. I smiled and shook my head "no".

"Have one man." He gestured to the rest of the beers on the table, with the one he was holding in his hand.

"Runners don't drink alcohol Daddy." I answered.

"Ya don't drink?" He asked cautiously.

"No Daddy."

"But I hear ya rale grown now?" He said.

"No Daddy, I no rale grown tall."

"Well dats what I hear ya na."

"Not me."

"Me an yu madda, we don't mind ya growing up ya na," He said. "We expect it. Ya been away a long time. Yu is eighteen, ya must grow."

As he spoke his dark skin glistened under the light of the patio that sat almost above his head. The top of his head, just in the center once full of thick tight curls, now looked like a sparse beaten path. I hugged myself and listened. I heard his heavy heart.

"One ting I come fi tell ya. Ya didn't come here to make babies non tall. You come here to be a champion. So don't tink you coming back to Trinidad with ya tail between ya legs. There are a lot of people who risk a lot to give you an opportunity to make di best out of ya life. Ya know what happened to Derby when he came back home?" I shook my head slowly.

"He was put on suspension for di rest of the year when you didn't come back with di team. How a man give up feeding his family for a stranger? Not to mention dese fine people who took a stranger into their home, and treat ya like their own, and the many others who put it all on di line betting on you Amy. I can't make you not take on dis distraction ya na. Dat is up to you to decide. A jus here to let ya know, no one can eat a whole pie all at once. Ya must do it one slice at a time. From where I'm standing ya trying to eat di whole pie. I want you to think about dese three questions before you continue eating pie."

"What's di worst thing that could happen ya now wid dis distraction?"

"What can't you see?"

"And what can others see?"

I started to answer him, but he stopped me. "This is something to think about," he said as he pointed to his temple with one finger. "Unless you've thought about dese questions before, ya not ready to answer them. Dem is not simple questions ya na."

Since my dad's visit, I asked Faith to take me back to see my doctor. The plan was for me to get started on oral contraceptive when I got my next menstruation and I refrained from sex. This was a shock.

I didn't tell coach that I was pregnant. I told him the doctor said everything was fine and that it must have been because I was dehydrated. The wrinkles in Coach's forehead relaxed.

When I got home it was already late afternoon and Faith was heading out with Lauren and Ruth for cheerleading practice. She stopped to hug me. She looked like a summer picnic advertisement dressed in jeans shorts just above her knees and a baby pink button up shirt. The only thing missing was her picnic basket.

"I heard you were dehydrated," she said with concern. "So I put one of your Gatorades in the freezer to cool down fast."

"Thanks."

"No problem. It's pasta night, so when I get back we'll have some real dinner. Are you okay?" She added. I managed to smile and nodded a yes.

I think Faith realized that my eyes avoided hers and she quickly asked, "Why don't you come with me?" She turned and grabbed the Gatorade out of the freezer with one hand and then my arm with the other. I slowly dragged myself out of the house, as she yelled to coach that I was going with her and the girls.

Lauren had already hopped out of the house and Ruth dragged her blanket out behind her. In the minivan Lauren and Ruth sat in the middle seats. Lauren was tall for her age and she fit right into her seat belt, but Ruth needed a booster seat. I sat in the front passenger seat and looked out the window. I tried to pretend that everything was okay, but it was hard. Tears rolled down my face as Faith drove the five minutes to practice. Lauren was asking a lot of questions like she always does, and Ruth sucked her thumb and rubbed her pink furry blanket. Faith put on a video that always distracted Lauren; "If You Give a Pig a Pancake". Immediately, they both started jamming to that music video. Faith kept her eyes on the road as she asked questions. "You looked like someone just told you it was the end of the world. Are you okay?" I shrugged my shoulders.

"Are you?" I shook my head back and forth.

"No."

"Is it what I think it is?"

"Yes."

"How?"

"I don't know."

"I'll make an appointment with my gynecologist for tomorrow and see how far along. Don't worry. We will be here for you."

"Don't tell coach."

"You gotta let him know."

"He is going to be disappointed, so please don't tell him yet. Let me think this through."

"Okay, and your dad?"

"My dad is going to kill me, so please let me think this through before you tell anyone."

"I get it."

At the gynecologist visit I learned that I was five weeks pregnant. Her words hit me like an electrical shock and it jolted my entire body. My reaction made the doctor ask me what my plans were. My whole life had been playing out before me for the past couple of days. As I sat on the examination table in the doctor's office, I looked out the window as she spoke. Her office was on the twenty first floor with a distant but clear view of the Hutchinson River. The dark blue water in the rivers quivered under a bridge.

From the doctor's office where I was and the side of the bridge where the blooming sycamore trees stood tall and strong, I saw rows of empty barren buildings on the other end of the bridge. Looking out at the bridge, I was reminded of the place I travelled many miles from and the circumstances that brought me here.

Over the vibrant blue Atlantic Ocean from a land full of very proud people, to a land that was filled with opportunity. I left the comfort of the Caribbean sun, the comfort of my family, my friends, and many teammates to be the one that should have made a difference not only in my life but in theirs as well. I wanted to hear what the doctor was saying, but the sound of my father's voice was louder instead and tears rolled down my face.

"What are di worst things that could happen?"

"What can't you see?"

"And what can others see?"

I thought of the worst things that could happen, and to me, that was getting pregnant. So I made plans to start taking contraceptives. Too late.

Now as I reflected, being pregnant was by far *not* the worst thing that could have happened. The worst thing that could have happened was having my family and all who sacrificed for me disappointed in me. I thought of what I couldn't see. It was too premature for me to see the pain of having things my way, of living away from my parent's constant advice and in my own autonomy. I thought about what others could see. I thought everyone saw me as the product of hard work and a dream. Now, I was afraid the only image they would see was me as a pregnant runner in the Olympics; or me not running at all. All the time, effort, and resources wasted on me; it looked like I'd be going back home to Trinidad for my father to kill me or for me to catch his runaway goats. Either way, that is not the life I was destined for.

I knew it was a privilege to have the opportunities that I had been given; an opportunity to be great. I knew me being successful was just as possible as it wasn't. I knew my Coach's story; how his hard work and determination took him to the Olympics in Moscow, Russia in 1980, but his injuries prevented him from running. He left America with his chest puffed up and feeling great. Then came back with his head hanging. I knew I had to be disciplined, dedicated, patient, and prepared to attain it. I worked daily at it, following coach's workout and nutritional advice, knowing that there were no guarantees even when others around me insisted that there were. I also knew that if I wanted a good chance, then I had to give it all up. I got distracted.

I heard the doctor's voice say, you have a choice. At that moment I decided.

***

When Amy finished her story, Eva got up from around the table, walked over to her and hugged her. "Yes we do," she said. "And where are you now?"

"I am good. I made the best decision for me."

"Why do you think about it all the time?"

"Because I am always grateful that I had a choice." Eva smiled, as she nodded her head. We all took turns hugging Amy. "You have amazing strength," I said.

***

Rain sat restless and uncomfortable in her chair while everyone told their story. She moved her head back and forth and side to side. When the tears began to swell up around her eyes, she closed them. The tears leaked out in big full drops. Softly she flicked her wrist from the folds of her arms and wiped her face gently.

When Eva asked, "Are you ready to tell your story?", she hugged herself tighter, lowered her head to one shoulder, shook her head no and covered her face with the palm of one hand. We all took turns comforting her and hugging her as if she had just poured out all her heart and soul. Her unspeakable words were loud, and the pain and hurt she was feeling was seeping out of every pour. It was evident that she was not ready. When

Eva stood her up and hugged her, she hummed a fitful cry. "It's okay." Eva whispered. "It's okay."

She began to rock Rain and whispered some more. "It's okay. Seek therapy, seek therapy, seek therapy, seek therapy, seek therapy, seek therapy, seek therapy, please." She released her back in her chair.

Rain's Story
Dear Mommy

When I got pregnant with my first child, a man who was a friend of the family tried to rape me. I used everything in me to protect my baby. An overwhelming strength that I didn't know I had came over me and I made me and my baby safe. It wasn't easy for me, but I found the strength to use my voice; so, I told an adult. Her response shocked me and cracked the very foundation that I had just begun to repair. I knew then that I had to survive to protect my children and to keep them safe.

Protecting my children wasn't always easy, but it was easier than being a mom. For me being a mom isn't easy, it's like living a double life. For the past twenty-three years I've been living a double life.

Becoming a mother was one of the hardest transitions of my life. Becoming a mother made me nervous. Becoming a mother made me scared. Would I know how to get this thing out of my damn body? Would I be able to take care of this thing? Would I be able to breastfeed this thing? Would I know how to love this thing?

Then it happened. I call it a miracle. My body opened up and gave me the most beautiful and perfect baby one could ever ask for. I spent every waking moment worrying about her care. Did I overfeed her? Did I put her to sleep in the right position? Did I hear her make a sound in her sleep? Did I make her cry? Did I put too many clothes on her? Did I take too many clothes off?

She was always in my thoughts and every sound she made grabbed my attention. She slept long predictable hours at first and then she changed her mind and slept whenever she damn well pleased. Then she cried all the time for no reason at all; before being fed, after being fed, it didn't matter. I swaddled her with kisses and kept her in my arms. I tried to figure out what could be wrong. I wasn't sure what to do to make her stop crying and go to sleep, so I did what I thought I should do. I rocked her, and paced back and forth until she exhausted the night and the morning lulled her back to sleep. I am a mother and she will know that I will always be there; always.

Motherhood made me anxious and happy; anxious that something would happen at any moment and take me away from my baby, but happy about the way she looked at me. Her smile melted my heart. I was happy that she depended on me. Happy that I could provide all her comfort; the kind that made her stretch her little fingers and grip them onto mine and hold on strongly.

Overnight she turned into a rambunctious toddler. She started to refuse to hold my hands when she walked. Then she refused to let me feed her, and refused my help with dressing her. She insisted on doing everything on her own and waged a war when I pushed back. I quickly learned who was in charge, so I had another child to fill my void.

My husband, like me, was happier with each child. Before you knew it, there were four. They were all girls. Each one came out different from the one before; different mood and very different personalities. The children kept us busy and that was good for us. We had very good excuses why we couldn't talk to each other, and even better reasons to be frustrated with one another. To preserve our family, we kept our communication to bare minimum. Only sarcasms, insults, and accusations that burned like the pleasant, but strong smell of the eucalyptus oil; the accusations were pleasant because it meant he knew I was still attractive and could take my heart and give it to whomever I wanted, but it still hurts that his thoughts were so limited. I longed to hear an adult's voice in our home. However, every word he said filled up my head nauseating me for days.

My heart broke when he left, but my soul rejoiced. Even though I had been lonely for years, this loneliness was frightening. I didn't know how to move on with four children by myself. I didn't know how I would meet their needs. On the days when I could get out of bed, I sat around the house in a blanket made into a robe. By the time I had enough energy to walk to the living room and watch TV. Jerry Springer was on. I couldn't find enough energy to go to work or send my children to school that day. I lifted my head from my chest in time to check on their muted presence. They moved their lips to get my attention, and I forced a gentle smile their way and sat back in the sofa. I don't remember what they ate or how I fed them. I do remember when I cried, they cried.

His hateful words replayed all the time in my head and it kept me hypnotized and immobile. One of my sisters came to visit, and she dragged me out of bed. She bathed my children and combed their hair. Then she bathed me and washed my hair, all while telling me silly jokes. By the weekend, we were going out of the house to a party. We went to loud bars, and louder clubs, but nothing made me forget his words. I kept going because I wanted something to cure me and take away his loud stupid voice from repeating in my head, but nothing quieted his words. So, I made a decision to get better. I didn't need the parties. They were useless. I was done with that. I wanted to get better for my children.

My sister had awakened me in time for me to clean up the mess. I cleaned up the house, sent my children to school, and went back to work. I still had crying spells, but I cried only when I was in my bedroom or when I was absolutely by myself. Whenever anyone questioned my mood or energy, I told them I had a headache. I told my doctor about what I was feeling and she prescribed me some antidepressants. To my surprise I felt much better after a month or so.

Many years later, I am a mother and a stepmom, a teacher, a doctor and a grandmother for my tribe. Still, the life I portray in front of my kids, family, and friends is totally different from the life I live when I'm by myself or when I'm home in my room. When my kids or my step kids are around I'm happy and I put my best face on. I laugh at their jokes and listen to their problems. One can't possibly live without the new IPhone, another can't find the perfect prom dress, the boys in school are crazy, the girls in school are nuts, and the gym teacher wrote up another for not changing into "proper gym attire".

"And that is not my fault, because all the gym teachers have known since the 9th grade that I don't get dressed in gym clothes on the first Monday of the month, because I ain't sweating out my silk press that I just got over the weekend."

"All I know is if you fail gym, I'm kicking your ass. You betta walk that stage."

"Have I ever?"

Nothing bothers me when I am interacting with them. In fact, to me it is one of life's pleasure and one that I look forward to. To be the one that they call on to listen to their foolishness. To be the one to protect them and the one that they can rely on. It is indeed a pleasure. It always has been.

When they were young it was their sweet smell that comforted me, or their whining cry. I never got tired of giving them all of me; and all of me they took. Once I had firm tight skin all over, and then the first child came and my body changed. With each child, my body changed. I can look down on my body and tell you which child gave me what stretch mark. It's a prize I gladly accept from each of them, and one of the reasons I look at them with so much admiration. Their becoming was also mine.

Although they are my joy, whether I'm with them or not, I always feel vulnerable. When I'm alone, I bask in the darkness. I need the blackness to comfort me and lull me to sleep. Though the darkness is sweet, because I know with it sleep will come and the noise will go away, it is also overwhelming in the minutes that I wait. Memories of my life's pain comes rushing through at me; each one trying to get me to pay more attention to.

The man who molested me as a child stands over me, so I close my eyes real tight and wait for him to go away. Sometimes he leaves quickly and sometimes without warning he walks towards me. His presence is frightening and I know it's time to start saying my prayers. As soon as he disappears I hear my ex-husband's shouts. If his shouting gets too loud I know it's going to be a long night. I get up and walk into the kid's room and watch them sleep. The night lamp shoots up the wall and as I walk in, it cast a shadow. I know they are safe. I know they are at peace. Eyes closed, mouths open, all of them are at peace. Then I'm grateful. Then I can attempt to sleep again.

Not even when I was young did I have the peace they lay with, sleep with, complain with, laugh with, and fight with. My peace, if ever was short lived. As soon as I thought that I was safe, I was reminded of the danger that lurked, waiting to shut me down.

192

When I was a child, as soon as I could understand, I noticed that everyone in my home had a mama, but no mommy. I lived with my grandparents; my grandmother was called mama and my grandfather was called dada. There were many of us in that home; my two brothers and two sisters and about umpteen cousins. None of us had a mommy, so I knew that was fine. Then I went to school, and some of the children had grown ups waiting to take them home. They called them mommy, so I asked my grandmother for my mommy. I was told that when I was a baby, my mommy went to America to prepare a home for me and my sisters and brothers. One day she was going to come back for all of us and take us to the home she was preparing.

I don't remember ever having a mommy, but going away with one made me excited. So, I waited for her to come. I told all the kids in school that one day soon I would not come back to class; that I had a mommy in "farin" and she would be coming back for me to take me and my sisters and brothers to our new home. I told everyone I saw, even the grownups. They were happy for me too. Some of them said they couldn't wait to see my mother again. I was surprised that they knew her, but they made me hopeful. I believed that one day I too would have a mommy and everything would be perfect!

When Mommy left for farin, I was just one year and six months old. I always thought that if I had a mommy, I would have never been molested and she would protect me, and I would never have to go get pepper. That man would have never taken his thing out of his pants and put it on my private. I thought, if I had a mommy, I would tell her about that man. I waited for

mommy to come to my school and pick me up to take
me to the home in America.

One day I had a cousin come to visit mama. She was
with her mommy and she called our grandmother mama
also. Her mommy was beautiful. She had big brown
eyes, and dimples on her cheeks. When she saw me, she
picked me up and swung me around, hugged me and
kissed me. She swung me just like some of the
mommies do when they came to pick up their kids at
school. She smelled like a sweet plum, freshly ripe.

I loved my cousin who came to visit mama with her
mommy, but I also envied her because she was the only
cousin I knew who had a mommy. She also didn't have
a sister or a brother like me and the rest of my cousins.
She was happy to play and happy to share her mommy.
We chased each other in the grass whenever she brought
her mommy. When I fell and scraped my knee, her
mommy kissed my scratch. I closed my eyes and wished
she was my mommy, kissing my scratched knee. With
my eyes closed I imagined telling my cousin's mommy
that no one needs pepper and I imagined she would
agree.

As I waited for Mommy to come and get me, both
my sisters left to go live elsewhere with one of our other
aunts. I didn't see them much. There were no other girls
in our house; just me and the umpteen cousins. I fought
with the boys and played with the boys. I got strong and
no one could make me get pepper again. I just said no
and no one could make me.

One Sunday evening, I was on the veranda playing
jacks when one of my aunts arrived in a red Volvo. She

swayed out of the car grabbing her maxi and walked heavily up the steps that led to the veranda. She smiled at me and went straight to my grandmother. I heard her say that she received a telegram that someone died in a car accident. At first I wasn't sure who she was talking about. Then she came over to me, hugged me, and whispered to me that my mommy just died in a car accident. My mind started to race and I couldn't think straight. Lots of thoughts flooded my mind. I always imagined that one day I would be in school and my mommy would just show up and I would be so surprised and so happy. I would tell everyone goodbye, because I was going to farin to live with my mommy.

I didn't understand what would happen, but I remembered when my cousins' mother died, they put her in a coffin, and put the coffin in the ground. They put dirt all over her. We never saw her again, so I got upset. There was so much I had planned to say and do with my mommy. My dreams of her swinging me around, kissing my knees when I fell and scraped them, came to an end.

My heart was so heavy. It was saying so much, but nothing came from my lips. My eyes swelled up with tears and I shut them real tight and laid curled up on my grandmother's bed. Who did she think she was, to leave me in this mess?

I went to America. I went to go to Mommy's funeral. I wrote everything I wanted to say to her when I saw her in her coffin. I wanted to be certain that my voice didn't get silent when the words rushed to my brain. So I wrote her a letter.

Dear Mommy,

*I am sorry you didn't find a home for me and my
sisters and brothers to live in, in America before you
died. I wish I remembered your face. I hope you had
dimples on each cheek, like your sisters and I hope you
remember my face. I have dimples on my cheeks too.
Mamma says I look just like you. I wish I met you before
you died in a car accident, but I am glad we never met
and I never had to tell you all the things that made me
cry at nights. You would surely cry. I wish we didn't
have to put you in the ground and put dirt all over you.
Don't be afraid mommy. One day you will come back.
My Sunday school teacher said one day the dead in
Christ shall come back to life.*

Love from your daughter that you named Rain.

When I came to America, I came to go to my
mommy's funeral. When I asked, 'when is the funeral?'
my aunt said that Mommy was already buried into the
ground.

In America, my mother's pictures were all around.
She had big brown eyes and dimples on her cheeks. I
walked into her room and it smelled like sweet ripe
plum. I closed my eyes, sucked up the air into my lungs,
and filled it up so I could carry her smell with me. There
was an attic closet and I walked into it. She had shoes
neatly tucked to the back of the wall and spread out from
one corner of the attic to the other, many different
colors. She had a brown leather bag with a golden latch
on the front sitting on top of a red suitcase with brown
corners and two brown belts running down the middle.
She had dresses, pants, and blouses. I looked up to the

lightbulb and I saw her hats stacked up beside her sweaters. Those must have been the hats she wore to church. They were lace, feathered, and flowered. On the left of the attic closet was a shelf with books. I picked up the red leather one. It read, "My damn diary. Open if you dare." I gasped and the book fell. I picked it up and quickly put it back on the shelf. Then I chuckled. I believe I really did have a mommy.

Back home, my sisters had left our grandparents to live with some of my dimpled aunts, but I stayed with my two brothers and my umpteen cousins. In this American home, I had four sisters and three brothers. One of my brothers did not get to come to America because there was a problem with his birth certificate. I shared a room with the two new sisters I had just met, because we were closer in age. They showed me the park where they played. This place was wonderland. It had things that I had never seen and wouldn't even have imagined. Colored slides and swings, monkey bars and merry-go-rounds, seesaws and basketball hoops. The park was filled with so much laughter it vibrated through you and came out when you least expected it. The laughter didn't frighten me, but it always surprised me. The playground was one of my favorite places to go.

Then one day I saw fear at the park and it made me feel unsafe. He was thirteen years old and I was eleven. He was playing basketball and the ball rolled over to where my little sisters were playing. One of my sisters grabbed the ball and attempted to bounce it, but before she could the ball player snatched it so hard it landed her clear over to the sandbox, on the other side of the playground. Everyone saw her fly across the park and slide on the asphalt, and they ran to help her. I ran up to the ball player and balled up my fist.

"Sa yu sorry!" I yelled.

"And if I don't what cha gonna do?"

"Sa yu sorry!"

By this time a crowd had formed around us and I was just waiting with all my heart for him to do something stupid. "Get outta my way, ya little twerp." He said as he swat at me as if I were a pesky fly.

I released all of the force in me right into his stomach and it curled him over. As he came down, I gave him a knee in his face and he fell out on the playground. I jumped on his head and grabbed him by his pants and dragged him over to my sister.

A woman picked me up off of him as I yelled.

"Sa yu sorry!!"

She grabbed my sisters and ushered us out the park.

"Go home quickly!" She rushed us off. I took my sisters and we walked off like I was a champ; each sister on one side and my hands in theirs. In that moment I felt victorious and safe.

One day, when I was thirteen years old, I was home when a tall dark skinned man came through the door. As he got closer, my lungs filled with heat and my blood started to boil. I felt my heart swelling up and I couldn't breathe. In front of me was one of my molesters. As I steamed up, the words in me evaporated. "Say hi likkle girl and stop staring. This is yu cuzzin." My Aunt Rose said. As she spoke I felt the steam in me explode and it ran down my legs. I ran off to my room and locked myself away for days. I came out only to use the bathroom. My sisters brought food to my room, but I just laid there stuck in my bed, unable to move. Sometimes I wanted to close my eyes but I couldn't, and the tears rolled out the side. The tears fell to the side of my face when I could only find the energy to lay on my back. When the pain was so great and it tangled up in my stomach, I curled up and brought my knees up to my chest to relieve the pain. The tears continued to roll down my face and onto my cheeks.

Days passed and my aunt told me if I needed someone to talk to, then I should talk to my big sisters. They didn't live with us anymore and I didn't trust anyone. My little sisters stayed with me and did their best to take care of me. Everything in me hurt. I had headaches and unbearable belly pain that made me cry and unable to eat. My brothers and sisters would come up to my room and talk to me, but even though I wanted to, I couldn't speak back to them.

One day one of my big sisters came to visit and someone told her I had been sick for three days and hadn't gotten out of bed. She sat on my bed and told me a story about a teenage girl who won a beauty contest and travelled the world in a golden cruise ship. When she went to Marbella, Spain she met a Spaniard Prince who stole her heart. He bought her everything she wanted and whatever he wanted her to have. Then he left with her on the golden cruise and travelled the rest of the world. She wiped my face and fed me chicken foot soup and chocolate candy. Then she put me in the shower and washed my hair. She dressed me and put me on her back, bringing me down the stairs and on to the front porch. The sun was shining brightly on the flowers in the garden and they all looked happy to be there. My sisters played double dutch in the streets with the neighbors and I was happy to see it all. I still have days when I feel like I am sinking into a dark hole, but on those days I read Psalms 91, *"He that dwelleth in the secret place of the Most High shall abide under the shadow of the almighty."* Selah.

***

After Rain spoke, Eva smiled at her and said, "I don't know where your resilience comes from, but I thank God you're here. Thanks for opening up about your experience. I know it wasn't easy for you."

When evening came at the end of what felt like our cleansing, everything around us was drenched in tears. The table, napkins, our sleeves, the Persian rugs on the floor beneath us; everything was wet. There was not a dry eye or nose in the house. Even the governess was standing in the adjoining room wiping her eyes. We were hugging each other, saying sorry and making promises. The governess came forward and directed us to the living room with the golden brown and tan velvet settee. Eva and Peaches went around handing out the little colorful gift bags.

"You are all beautiful, inside and out," Eva said. "What you have been through has been tough. Asking you to tell your stories is not to awaken anger, rage, or sadness in you. It is to allow you to consciously think about where you are coming from. For you to intentionally reflect upon the emotions you may have had during your experience, or emotions you may have never felt before. Asking you to tell your stories is to give you a forum to express something that is important to you, in a setting that feels safe. It is to let you know that we all hurt. We all have a story. Our stories are different, but they are all important. It is important for each of us to tell our own stories when we are damn good and ready. Thinking back on your stories should give you validation that you are equally strong as a rock and fragile as an egg. And guess what? It is your responsibility to stay strong and to protect your fragility.

"How do you do that?" Rain asked.

"Be there for each other." Eva responded.

"Take care of yourself first."

"Say no sometimes, even to the people you love."

"Especially to the people you love."

"Get your hair done."

"Dance."

"Laugh."

"Be kind to children."

"Accept kindness."

"Pass it on."

"Respect yourself."

"Honor yourself."

"Yes!" Peaches shouted. "I love it. I promise you if you guys come back next year, I will share my story."

We all smiled. Eva added. "We stay strong by constantly healing and we heal by reflecting on where we are mind, body, and soul. We heal by giving to others, even when we feel like giving up. We heal by being grateful for everything we have, and everything we desire."

"Everyone should have a therapist or a life coach to help them stay consistent, because life happens and then all of a sudden weakness slips in and your healing is compromised." Peaches assured us.

Eva continued, "We protect our fragility by being true to ourselves. Don't make things seem worse than they are, but look at things the way they really are. Know that no matter what the facts are or the circumstance, it is only another tool for God to work his wonders in your life. All things work for good for those that love the Lord. *Selah*."

The evening came and it was time for us to go home.

About the Author

Denise Nicholson is the co-founder of Knitted Together, a company specializing in healing from trauma through therapeutic storytelling and empowerment programs. She is also the founder of Seeds of Opportunity which is a nonprofit organization whose goal is to give impoverished children a chance to succeed by providing basic needs and focusing on enhancing their education.

Denise is known as an inspirational and insightful speaker with gift of telling stories. She is a native of Jamaica, West Indies and migrated to New York as a teenager. She became a teenage mother who then overcame many obstacles to become an entrepreneur. She is a registered nurse by trade, a board certified family nurse practitioner and doctoral candidate at Pace University.

DENISE NICHOLSON